TYSON &
JOEY

TWO WORLDS COLLIDE

TOM WATTS

TYSON & JOEY

Tyson & Joey

Two Worlds Collide

by Tom Watts

Published by

Tom Watts

Copyright © 2016 Tom Watts

ISBN: 9780648027706

Cover by Red Raven Book Design

Editing by Gregory Porter

V6

Contact information - email: tomjwtts@gmail.com

TYSON & JOEY

Contents

TYSON & JOEY

1

Tyson

A hush descended upon the auditorium as the young man stepped onto the stage, seemingly oblivious to the welcoming applause that had recently filled the room. A serious character, it seemed, with a furrowed brow and slightly downturned mouth. It was clear that the speaker meant business, but beyond that, his face appeared unreadable to the assembled masses.

"Thank you for coming today," he began, as he stepped up to the microphone. "I appreciate it. When I've finished speaking, you'll understand why your attendance is so important to me. I'll take some questions after my speech, but I only have two rules – no asking about my past, and no asking about my plans for the future. It's not because I'm ashamed of my history. Far from it. And my future isn't my concern right now. I have no idea what it holds, and you know what? That's just fine with me. I stand by these rules, though. I hope you can respect them, as if you fail to do so, it may suggest that everything I'm about to tell you is for nothing."

The young man paused, sipping at a glass of water. The atmosphere was thick with intrigue, and the audience remained on tenterhooks, awaiting the commencement of his address.

"OK, let's get started. Before we get to the real heart of my story, you should know a little about me. I used to keep a journal, which I completed at the end of each day. It seemed important to me. When you hear about the kind of life I lived, you'll understand why. Some may have used it as evidence, some could have found it inspirational, and to others still it would be a cautionary tale. The perspective you take is yours, and yours alone. This is an extract from one of the final entries I made – a summary of a day in my life. My *old* life, from what feels like a long time ago. This was written shortly before my circumstances changed forever."

Clearing his throat, the man began to read.

"I wake to the sound of a screaming baby and kids running up and down the hallway. I live on the ninth floor of a social housing building, sharing the space with my mother and younger sister. My father left when I was twelve, so I'm the man of the house. It's a role I take seriously. Certainly more than *he* ever did.

I rise out of bed and stare out of the window at the streets below. They're beginning to show life. Rubbish trucks pass, people begin the commute to work, and shopkeepers lift the cages on their stores. The homeless who have found a night's rest in the shop front are moved on without a second thought, or any risk of compassion.

Another day in paradise.

I'm born and raised in Trentan, an inner-city district known for its high crime rate and not much else. The community has been neglected. Everything here, from the roads to the services, is in a state of disrepair. Life is hard.

After working all night, I've only managed a few hours of sleep. I make my money selling drugs. It's dangerous work, but I'm good at it. In Trentan, that's reason enough to carry on.

I'm a product of my environment. Not by choice, but as a result of been raised in a broken home in a low-income area. My life of crime was set in motion long before I could make a conscious decision.

From a young age, I was exposed to things that no kid should see. There were good times for sure, but things could turn violent at any point. One minute you're playing with your friends on the street. The next you're witnessing a murder over drugs. And sometimes, what went on in the house was even worse.

These memories stick with you, and in many ways they harden you. Constantly seeing people die or taken away by the police makes you see life as temporary and unforgiving. Subconsciously, this makes you live for the moment. You never know when your time might be up.

With that mentality, you don't think long term. You look for quick success. You can't afford to take your time and establish a career; money is needed *now*. Selling drugs is the natural progression. Drugs are everywhere in Trentan, and there's always a market for them.

I'm stuck in a cycle perpetuated by poverty and fear. I know if I stop selling, my family will end up homeless. I can't let that happen. If I don't support them, nobody will. Not my Dad. Not the government. Nobody. This keeps me doing what I'm doing. I don't see any other option.

The way I see it, young men in Trentan are destined for one of a few fates. Some become casualties of the street life, killed by a rival dealer or crazed feign. Others are caught up in the prison system, and enter an eternal cycle of going away and coming home. A few are forced into low-income jobs, just about keeping their heads above water. And many become strung out on drugs.

Very few transcend this environment, and those that do usually don't come back to show others how. Without access to real opportunities and positive role models, everything stays the same here. One generation after the other falls into the same traps.

Drugs and alcohol are rotting the community at its very core. For many, reality is too harsh to look directly in the eye, so they try to escape it. Looking to temporarily numb their pain, and quickly becoming addicted in the process. I serve these fiends on the street every night, and see first-hand how addiction destroys their lives. For this reason, I never touch the shit. I can't afford to end up like them and risk losing my family.

Then there are those who turn to religion. Faith has a strong presence within the community. I guess it provides people with a sense of hope. People pray for things to get better. That's how I see it anyway.

These are the vices of the community. There are liquor stores, drug dealers and churches on every corner. Out of desperation, people reach for one of them. Trying to find some respite from the feeling of hopelessness that pervades the entire neighbourhood.

Not me, though. I know that reaching for these vices only leads to more suffering. If I am ever to transcend this reality, I have to stay strong and not grow dependent on any one thing.

I've developed my own code of living out here. One based on the core principle of living in the present moment. No matter how harsh things get, no matter what situation comes into my life, I will see it in it's fullest and take action accordingly.

Living like this puts me in touch with my instincts. I navigate the chaos of my environment by trusting them fully, knowing that they are guiding me in the right direction. It's a moment-by-moment way of being, one that enables me to read situations and anticipate change. For instance, I can tell when things are about to turn violent, or if cops are present. It's like a sixth sense; I'm tapped into, and in tune with the streets. This gives me an advantage out here that's fundamental to my success as a dealer.

I also see the bigger picture of the drug game, and how my operation sits within it. I see the trends in the market. I pay close attention to the feigns, and look for any change in their palette. They're always after something new and exciting. That's human nature, and the effects of addiction. I utilise this knowledge, marketing my product accordingly. I'm a hustler and a businessman.

I know I've developed a powerful way of living, one that offers me survival and success in these streets. It's been forged through years spent on the corner, interacting with all walks of life and observing the dynamics of the community at large.

The present moment is all I have. Everything else is madness.

I observe this truth whenever my mind threatens to dwell on the past, or worry about the future. These things make me anxious and depressed about my life situation, and that leads to distraction – a death sentence in Trentan.

But If I stay present, focussed on the here and the now, those thoughts and feelings never have a chance to take root. I still learn from the past and plan for the future, but I do so practically, in the *now*.

I understand the dynamics of my own mind, and know it's my greatest challenge out here.

Living in the moment offers me peace. I can be surrounded by chaos in every capacity, but as long as I'm present I feel a connection to something bigger. Call it what you will; spirituality, God, the Universe. I sense it, and always have. My life on the surface may be constantly changing, but that peace is always there when I need it.

When I'm in touch with that peace, I feel as though I'm destined for greater things. As though there is a greater plan for me. The details of that plan are unclear, and I don't know what else I could do; the streets are all I know. That said, I trust and have faith that it will become clear in time. Hopefully *before* this lifestyle catches up with me.

I have plans of making enough money to move out of Trentan, and to provide my family the life they deserve. I want to apply my knowledge into something legitimate, deploy the business skills I have developed through running my drug operation. Counting cash, investing in product, marketing, expanding territory, hiring and firing workers; these are all part of my day-to-day business. Every aspect reflects the processes within a business, big or small. Knowing this gives me hope.

All I need is an opportunity.

When I'm completely honest with myself, and look closely at my situation, I see that I have reached a critical point in my life. I see that the path that I'm heading down is unforgiving, and *will* take me away from my family eventually. I know it's only a matter of time before I'm arrested or killed.

If I'm ever going to transcend this environment, I need to make a change soon."

2

Joey

A short drive from Trentan, just across the river that divides the city, lived Joey. Though similar in age to Tyson, this is where the parallels end. The two men lived in the same city, but it may as well have been different worlds. Leafy avenues with large houses of all designs and colours replaced the hard concrete streets and social housing buildings that defined the streets of Trentan, although the racial divide was just as evident. Joey and Tyson had one other thing in common, however; Joey too kept a journal. A record of a young man's pain and torment.

"I'd like to change tack a little now," Tyson announced to his audience. "I hold in my hand the journal of somebody very important to me – a very dear friend. He has kindly given me permission to share the contents of this diary, which by extension, means he has agreed to share the contents of his mind, heart and soul with all of you. No doubt, you will respect this bravery.

The reason I am sharing Joey's journal with you is

that I feel it will help you understand that things are not always what they seem, and surface appearances may be deceptive."

Allowing his words to sink in again, Tyson took a breath and once again began to read from the hand-written notebook before him.

"I wake after a long night of barely sleeping. Insomnia is becoming more and more present in my life. I just lie there, wide awake, desperate to get rest and switch off from my thoughts. I can't, though. I just *can't*.

I lay in bed late into the morning, contemplating whether to get up and go to class. I decide to skip it. Doesn't matter anyway. Who needs to know about business marketing? I couldn't give a shit about it. I only signed up for the course to keep my parents happy.

I finally get up and make my way downstairs, into the living quarters of the big empty house that I call home. My parents are out, and my sister at school, so I have the place to myself. I begin my morning routine that consists of coffee, cereal and mindlessly flicking through TV channels as I sprawl out on the couch.

Nothing excites me anymore. Not my course. Not my social life. Nothing gets me motivated and out of the door in the morning. I feel myself falling into a hole; the social, outgoing guy that used to love sports and hanging out with friends is slowly turning into a withdrawn and depressed young man.

Anxiety is becoming the backdrop of my life. The only place I feel comfortable is in solitude, away from people and places. I can't stand being around my friends, and I hate the person I'm turning into. I just want the old me back. The guy who was the life of the party, and was into everything.

What the fuck is happening to me?

I'm embarrassed by the way I feel. I know I have it good. My parents are well off and they give me anything I want or need; there are no worries in that department. That all just seems meaningless to me, though, regardless of how ungrateful that may sound. I need to find some peace, and I'm yet to find a credit card able to pay for that.

As the day draws on, the anxiety gets worse. By mid-afternoon, I can't take it any longer. I need some relief from the tightness in my chest, the pressure in my mind, and the constant, repetitive speeding of my heartbeat, like some kind of internal racetrack. So of course, I numb myself the only way I know how. The house has everything I need; a constant supply of alcohol and prescription drugs. Healthcare professionals may not recommend self-medication, but it sure is easy.

I take three of my Dad's heart pills, and wash it down with a stiff glass of rum. No one will notice. They never have.

Instant relief.

The edge is taken off. I sink back into the couch and continue to anesthetise myself for the afternoon ahead. Any lingering thought of making my lecture is gone.

The days have bled into weeks as I continue to sink deeper into depression and addiction. I've lost track of my routine altogether. My family are oblivious; they leave early and arrive late. They're too caught up in their own lives to notice anything wrong with mine. I prefer it that way. I want to be left alone.

Everything is grey and gloomy, and no light penetrates through. A feeling of hopelessness overwhelms me. I feel numb to my emotions, except anger. I feel angry about what is happening to me. *What did I do to deserve this?*

I had heard about mental illness, but never believed it would happen to me. I associated it with crazy people. *Mentally ill?* Just the term made me think of straightjackets and white padded rooms. *I don't have that shit. It must be something else.*

So I began to research. I spend countless hours online matching my symptoms to any number of psychological disorders. This was quite therapeutic, in a way. I wasn't aware of how many people out there were feeling just like me. Just knowing this gave me a sense of hope. Hope that I might rise out of this mental suffering.

Soon, this became my latest addiction. I spend my days liquored up, researching mental illness. Reading endless threads on people's experiences with all sorts of psychological disorders. Seeking comfort in experiences of others. There are no clear answers, though. Some people recommend medication, others tell you to stay clear of it. Others still have non-medicated approaches, and even spiritual solutions, all of which seem to have mixed results. *So what is it?* I know I need a professional opinion. Self-diagnosis on Google, along with self-medication, can only get me so far.

But what if I get thrown in the loony bin?

The fear of that alone is enough to put the idea on hold.

So I continue to self-prescribe with drugs and alcohol. I sink deeper and deeper in the grips of depression. I start contemplating a way out, but death seems to be the only route through the darkness. I can't believe I'm thinking this way, but I have no control over my mind. It has me convinced that death will free me from the pain and misery that I'm feeling.

If I don't get help soon I will be dead within the week.

This is the dominant thought in my mind.

But if I ask for help, I will end up like Jack Nicolson from One Flew Over the Cuckoo's Nest. Spending the rest of my life in white pyjamas, sedated on meds.

This is my dilemma while I sit drunk and drugged up on the couch of my living room. I contemplate my future.

Suicide or a mental institution. This is all my mind will allow me to see, and I believe it. Those are my options. Nothing more, nothing less.

People are now beginning to notice the change in me. My family comment on my weight loss. I have hardly eaten in the past few weeks. Drugs, alcohol and cigarettes have become my staple diet. I don't even care about personal hygiene anymore. I have no respect for myself.

"Are you alright son? You're looking rather pale and thin?" my father commented as we passed each other in the hallway.

"I'm all good," is all I could muster the energy to reply. But that's all he needed. No more questioning from Dad. We were already teetering dangerously close to an actual, emotional conversation.

It's 4am and I can't sleep, even after multiple sedatives. The addiction of cigarettes draws me out of bed.

I sit heavily in the outdoor patio chair, head drooped between my legs. Cigarette in my mouth, and the standard glass of booze at my side.

I bring the cigarette to my arm and push it hard against the skin until it goes out. The pain makes me feel alive for a brief moment.

This is it. I will be gone soon. Suicide is calling.

Everywhere I look, I see ways that I could end it right now.

But how am I thinking this way? How did things escalate to this?

I have absolutely no perspective on my situation.

When I look in the mirror, all I see looking back is a shadow of my former self. An empty vessel, with no life inside. I want to cry but I can't. I just stare back at the face of a stranger. Hoping and wishing that things will return to normal. Whatever normal is.

I can't live with myself anymore."

3

Two Worlds Collide

The audience were enraptured by Tyson's vernacular loops, but they had heard only the beginning of the story. There was much to learn about how Tyson and Joey grew to enter each other's lives and the impact they had on one another. To fully understand how Tyson ended up speaking to his captive audience, some background information was essential, and he began to tell the abridged story.

It was Friday, his busiest night of the week. The local feigns would be out as usual, but there would be additional traffic from businessmen and college kids, stopping through Trentan to score drugs for the weekend. This is where the real money came from, so it was essential that his product was ready to go.

He went about his daily routine before getting ready for the night ahead. This consisted of getting his sister fed and packed off to school, and ensuring his mum had enough food and household items to get through the day. Once they were sorted, he would take care of himself and his crew. Family would always be his priority.

Tyson stayed disciplined in everything he did. Everything, from his family and crew to eating habits and workout routine. He prided himself on staying consistent, and giving attention to detail to all parts of his life. In the drug game, attention to detail could be the difference between life and death.

Now it was time to focus on his crew and product. First point of call, as always, was Jimmy. Tyson's right-hand man and confidante.

"Jimmy! How's everything looking for tonight? Did Stan come through with the product?"

"What time is it?" Jimmy replied, sounding half asleep, and clearly still in bed.

"Come on man, there's work to be done. You know you had to sort that product first thing."

"Alright, I'm up, I'm up! It'll be sorted, don't worry. You know I've got you. See you at the spot at five."

"Alright! Keep me posted on Stan."

Tyson continued to call around the crew, ensuring everyone was on for tonight. They were like brothers to him, and acted like it too. He had to be disciplined to keep order, but he also had to show them respect. Just like any business, without respect, recognition and reward, no employee is going to go the extra mile for you. In this line of work, you needed that more than ever. When things went south, Tyson trusted these guys with his life, and they trusted him with theirs.

All set for tonight. Family is taken care of, product sorted. The boys are ready to go. Now it's time to work out and hit the streets.

Across town Joey was going about his own daily ritual. Waking up late, rolling out of bed and making his way down stairs to lollop on the couch while feeding his ever-increasing addictions.

As he was fixing himself a drink in the kitchen the doorbell rang.

Fuck, what now? Probably a courier with more online crap for my sister.

"I'm coming, I'm coming!"

He dragged himself away from the drink to answer the door. Pulling it open, his best friend Sammy stood within the frame, visibly shocked by Joey's physical appearance.

"Shit, Joey! What happened? You look like you've lost some serious weight. Are you alright man?"

"Sammy? What the hell are you doing here?" Joey responded sheepishly, knowing full well that he had avoided and neglected his friend for weeks.

The reality of his situation sunk home at that moment. Seeing his best friend look at him with genuine concern quickly sobered him up.

"I'm sorry, mate. I've been seriously struggling."

Sammy came inside, and Joey told him everything about what he was going through. He began shaking and crying as he talked about his struggle with depression. Releasing the emotions that he had been holding in for so long like a pressure cooker that had been awaiting an opportunity to explode.

"Why didn't you tell me?" scolded Sammy. "My uncle went through something similar, you're not the only one. It's common. If there's one thing I learned from him it's that you need to communicate, Joey. You can't go through this bullshit alone."

"I know Sammy, but I was embarrassed. I felt weak and ungrateful, especially because I have it so good. Look at this house and the life I've been given. It just all seems so meaningless. The comfort makes no difference."

"That's some heavy shit man. It's hard to relate. I feel sad and unhappy sometimes but nothing like what you're describing. Sounds awful, man."

"It is! The feeling of absolute hopelessness is overwhelming. It's all consuming. My mind convinces me that there's no way out of it. Sounds crazy I know."

"You need help, Joey. You can't sit here numbing yourself. You'll end up getting hurt. Or worse."

"I know. But maybe that's what I want!"

"Snap out of that shit, *real* quick. Don't fucking talk like that. You're hanging with me tonight. I'm not leaving you alone. You need to get out of this house. I know a new bar across town, we can go check it out."

Joey tried to make up excuses about why he couldn't make it, but in the end agreed to hang out with Sammy. *Why not?* he thought. It was better than moping around the house, and at least he could drink. His contemplations of suicide and the mental ward could be put on hold, at least for the night.

"I'll pick you up at 7," Sammy said as he walked out the door, giving Joey no chance to reply.

Evening came and Joey started getting ready for the night ahead. As he did so, he felt an unfamiliar sensation of calm wash over him. It only lasted momentarily, but it was there. Before he had time to ponder the feeling, a car horn sounded outside.

"Beep! Beep!" Sammy's Camaro screamed loudly from the driveway.

Joey grabbed his things and made his way outside to find Sammy, accompanied by two other friends he hadn't seen in months. Craig and Manny were occupying the back seat, leaving the front for Joey.

"What's up, Joey?" Sammy shouted. "Let's get this show on the road."

"I'm coming, I'm coming…have some patience, shit!!"

The guys laughed as Joey slammed the car door and Sammy sped off into the night.

"First stop, Mohikas!"

Mohikas was a new bar that had just opened up across town. It was in the district of Dormanty, which sat on the outskirts of Trentan – or The Hood, as the comfortable suburbanites commonly referred it to. It was an old industrial area that had been subject to gentrification over the past decade. Old buildings had been re-developed into restaurants, bars and art galleries.

These days, it was the hottest spot in town. All the rich kids from the suburbs thought they were edgy partying in an area once renowned for violence. Dormanty was once overrun with pimps, prostitutes, feigns and dealers, though they had now migrated further south to Trentan. Sex and drugs would have been the only reason to visit in the past, but now rich kids could drink in the danger and decadence from a safe distance.

The boys steamed across the bridge, music blaring as they crossed into Dormanty. The place was alive with people. Bars and restaurants spilled onto the sidewalk, dragging in pedestrians as they walked past.

Sammy pulled into a parking space along the main drag and the boys hopped out. "Let's do this shit!" Sammy excitedly yelled at the top of his lungs, the poster child for youthful testosterone.

They were like a pack of wolves howling at the top of their lungs, whistling at groups of girls as they walked by. Joey didn't share the same enthusiasm; he was just eager to get into a bar and have a drink. The place was driving up his anxiety, especially the way the guys were clowning around. He needed something to take the edge off. Something strong.

Do nights like this help or hinder me? Joey found himself pondering.

After walking for a while, they were eventually directed to Mohikas. The bar was down an alleyway; narrow, covered in graffiti and dimly lit with only one way in and out, it was a scary sight.

Great! Joey thought. *We're just asking to get mugged.*

"I wonder how many people have been killed down here," Sammy asked half seriously, as the guys walked into the darkness.

Finally, they came to a door illuminating the name Mohikas.

"Thank fuck," Craig said, "let's get inside before we get killed."

"Knock! Knock!" They waited a moment before a slit in the door opened.

"Who is it?" a deep voice responded from inside the bar.

"Your Mama," Manny replied sharply.

A bolt on the door unlocked and the door opened slowly to the sound of hip-hop music and a large, unfriendly-looking bouncer.

"Who's been talking about my Mama?" he asked, without an ounce of humour in his voice.

The boys all pointed to one another.

"Funny guys, huh? I got no time for funny guys. Hurry up and get inside. Don't let me hear you talking about my Mama again."

"Shit! Can't Hagrid take a joke?" Manny mumbled as they walked through the door.

The bar was dark inside. The gang could barely see people's faces across the room. The atmosphere was relaxed, with punters kicking back in the big leather couches.

The boys didn't mess around; they were straight to the bar for a round of drinks.

"I need something strong," Joey voiced.

"How about shots?" Sammy suggested.

A quick cheers to salute the start of the night, and down the hatch the liquid went. Round after round, the boys took turns ordering a variety of drinks.

After a few hours at the club, they were becoming noticeably intoxicated. Craig was an obnoxious drunk, and as was standard he was beginning to irritate some of the other partygoers. It would only be a matter of time before he got kicked out. That was all par for the course on a boy's night out. At least one of the guys would be ejected at some point during the night.

The rule was simple; if someone was kicked out, you had to leave as well. The only exception was if you were on the verge of picking up. Joey was the ladies' man of the group, so this usually applied to him. Since the depression had taken hold, though, he barely even thought of girls. He barely even thought of anything anymore.

Eventually Craig was firmly told to leave, and the boys followed suit.

"See ya Hagrid! Your bar is shit anyway!" Manny yelled as he waved goodbye to the bouncer, who looked on unimpressed.

"Where to next?" Sammy asked.

They knew of another spot called Aberdene, about a ten-minute walk away. It required going further south which meant venturing closer to The Hood.

"This way!" Craig said confidently.

"Are you sure?" Sammy asked. "I thought the barman said it was down Clarkson Ave?"

"Nah, it's definitely this way," he insisted.

So off they went, full of liquor and confidence, singing and yelling through the streets as they stumbled towards the bar.

"Where is this joint?" Manny yelled out to the boys ahead after walking for ten minutes.

"Just a little further," Craig replied.

Up ahead were a number of state housing towers, a sight synonymous with Trentan.

"Are you sure?" Joey interjected. "This doesn't look like Dormanty. Hold on – this is Trentan! Let's get out of here before some shit goes down! We're not supposed to be here, man!"

As the boys turned to run back, they were confronted with the reality of their ignorance.

"You boys lost?" a voice echoed out of the darkness.

Standing in front of them was Tyson and three of his crew.

"*Are you boys lost*?" he repeated, an icy steel creeping into his voice.

"We're just looking for Aberdene nightclub," Craig

stuttered nervously.

Tyson and his crew started pissing themselves laughing.

"Aberdene nightclub! I don't think we got one of them in Trentan. Not enough rich kids here to spunk their parents' money on booze, y'know? You boys *are* lost."

All of a sudden, things turned serious. Tyson's crew instinctively moved passed him and started beating them to the ground, a flurry of fists and feet. Wallets and watches were snatched in the process.

Jimmy grabbed Joey by the scruff of the neck and pulled him to his feet, before holding a pistol to his head. The other boys screamed, scampered away and made a run for it, leaving Joey behind to face his fate.

"Is that what you call loyalty? They just left you to die," Jimmy muttered darkly, shaking his head while he pushed the nine-millimetre hard against Joey's temple. "Fucking rich kids. No sense of community."

Joey couldn't talk. He just gritted his teeth and closed his eyes while Jimmy continued to rant.

"Open your eyes, motherfucker. Look your killer in the eye. Show some respect, boy! You think it's a joke, coming up in our neighbourhood you ignorant son of bitch? Do you see us crossing the bridge and coming into your suburbs, motherfucker? Now you've forced me to make an example out of you," Jimmy shouted into his ear.

Joey had never been so afraid. He thought he was going to be killed right there on the spot. Suddenly, it was clear to him that death was *not* the solution he had been seeking.

"No!" Tyson shouted, putting his hand on Jimmy's shoulder and instructing him to lower the gun. "Leave him!"

Tyson looked Joey in the eyes and handed back his wallet and watch. "Go home."

Joey turned and ran as fast as he could, not even checking to see if the contents of his wallet had been liberated. Tyson turned and walked in the opposite direction, past Jimmy who had a confused look on his face.

"What the fuck, boss? Why did you let him go like that? He saw our faces!" Jimmy said heatedly.

Jimmy shot a single round into the air, expressing his frustration at his leader. Tyson didn't flinch and continued to walk calmly away.

"Go home!" he eventually yelled back. "Have the night off."

Joey stumbled as he heard the gun shot in the distance. Adrenalin pumped through his veins as he sprinted towards the lights of Dormanty. The boys were a couple of blocks ahead and immediately thought the worse when they heard the shot.

"Fuck!" Sammy screamed. "They got Joey, man. We got to go back."

"And get shot too? Fuck that shit!" Craig replied.

"Maybe it came from somewhere else? Could have been a car backfiring?" Manny suggested hopefully, seeing the look of terror in his friend's faces.

The boys were quickly sobered by the reality of the situation as they waited down a quiet backstreet, desperate for any sign of Joey. Eventually, they heard the sound of footsteps before a figure came screaming around the corner.

"It's Joey! Thank God you're alright, man!" Sammy shouted with a sense of relief.

Joey ran towards his friends, instructing them to run with panic in his voice. The quartet raced back to the nightclub district with a renewed urgency, with the bright lights and crowds of people a welcoming sight. They made it to the car and collapsed over the bonnet as they tried to catch their breath.

"What happened, Joey?" Craig eventually asked.

Joey didn't respond. He had his head hunched over, with his hands on his knees, drawing in deep breaths.

"How could you guys ditch me like that?" he quietly

asked. "I was lucky I wasn't killed! If it wasn't for the leader, that guy would have blown my head off."

"We panicked," Sammy said, feeling guilty for leaving his best friend behind. "I wanted to come back, I'm sorry man."

"At least no one got hurt," Craig said, attempting to ease the tension. "Though I'm gutted about my watch. That cost a fortune."

"I'm never following your directions ever again, Craig. You led us right into The Hood!" Manny shouted angrily.

"Fuck it!" Joey yelled. "What's done is done. I need some space. I'm going to find my own way home tonight. I can't be around you guys right now." Slowly gathering his composure, he stood up straight. "I'm glad we're all OK. You guys go home and let me be. We can talk about it tomorrow. Maybe."

"Alright, man. I know you feel betrayed, Joey…we're sorry," Sammy replied.

"I'm out!" Joey shouted back as he walked off into the crowded Main Street.

The guys did as Joey said and drove home, unconcerned about their intoxication levels. The car was in complete silence as they crossed the bridge back into the suburbs.

As Joey walked the streets trying to make sense of

what had just happened, he was overcome by a sense of *aliveness*. For the first time in as long as he could remember, his mind felt clear. The intensity of the situation had seemingly shocked him out of his depressive state.

He looked around, and simply appreciated his surroundings. No worries for the future, or thoughts of the past. He was *present*. His senses were heightened, picking up every noise, sight and smell. He felt completely connected to his surroundings.

What's happening to me?

Eventually, his thoughts began to take over. He could feel the clarity fading as he slowly lost touch with the moment and returned to his mind-identified state.

He knew that he had just experienced a glimpse of something special. In that brief moment, he had been free of the psychological suffering that had plagued his mind and connected to a space of clarity and peace. Overwhelmed by it all, he went and found a bench to sit on and attempted to compose himself.

Fuck me. I was almost killed.

He sat and replayed the night's events over in his mind. Rubbing his bruised temple from where the gun had been pressed, a physical reminder of what had transpired. That was when it started again; the racing heartbeat and sinking sensation in the pit of his stomach. The moment of clarity had passed.

I need to get home, he thought.

"Taxi!" he yelled as a cab passed by, outstretching his arm and grateful that his wallet had been returned. The carriage pulled over and he jumped in without hesitation. He felt numb as it peeled off into the night and made its way over the bridge. Staring blankly out the window into the darkness, he wondered what it all meant.

Why did they let me go? What was the peace I felt? He was mentally and physically exhausted by the experience. Once home, he collapsed on his bed and entered a deep sleep.

He woke the next morning to his mother rummaging through his room looking for dirty washing.

"Hey, Ma," he mumbled through a fug of sleep.

"Morning, baby boy. Big night out was it?" she replied, noting that he was still fully clothed.

"You have no idea," he mumbled as the events of the night came flooding back to him.

"Me and your sister are making pancakes if you're hungry. They'll be ready in half an hour," she called back to him as she left the room.

Joey slowly rose out of bed and jumped into the shower. *What a night,* he thought to himself as the water brought him out of his haze.

Envisioning the gun to his head gave him chills. He

had never been in a potentially deadly situation like that. That wasn't what dominated his thoughts, though. More than anything, he was touched by the experience that followed. The clarity that came over him and temporarily lifted him out of his depressive state.

What was happening to me?

In that moment, Joey had found relief from the torment of his mind. This gave him hope. Hope that, if he came to understand what had happened, he could in turn understand his psychological suffering.

On the other side of town, Tyson was grappling with his own issues regarding the events that had occured. Most of all, he was questioning himself. What had made him intervene? What had driven him to let the boy go and disrespect his crew? Was he growing soft, or was he realising the senselessness of it all?

Tyson lay in bed late into the morning, wrestling with his thoughts. He quickly began to feel a restrictive depression crush his chest as he dwelled on the past, and worried about the future. The reality of his life situation, and the problems that his community were facing, were too much. He could feel himself welling up and getting angry as he thought of his sister, his mum, and the people he had lost along the way. *Why do we have it so hard? Why? When people have it so good just across the bridge. Was it all an accident of birth? When will this shit change? It's hopeless!*

The pain was too intense for Tyson to bear. He needed to numb it. He climbed out of bed and padded to the cupboard that sourced his leftover product; that which hadn't sold the previous night. He knew it would make him feel better, at least in the short term. Hundreds of customers couldn't be wrong, after all. He lined up the white powder on his bedside table, rolling up a note to snort it with.

Is this really the answer?

Tyson hung his head over the narcotic as he weighed up the consequences of the decision he was about to make. Tears streamed down his check, splashing into the drugs as the pain flowed out of him.

"Fuck it!" he snapped. "Wake up!" he yelled at himself. Slamming his fist on the table and sending the powder flying.

"Snap out of it!" he repeated aloud. "The future and past are no place for you! Stay present...it's the only place you will find peace and make any real change."

Repeating this mantra to himself, Tyson rose to his feet and walked over to the mirror. Chin held high and chest expanded, he wiped the tears from his eyes and took a deep breath while looking at his reflection. Feeling strong again, he raised his arms and flexed his muscles, knowing he had just looked drugs in the eye and said no.

You're too strong for that shit. Nothing will stop you, none of these traps. I'm going to succeed and bring change to my family and community. Fuck anything and anyone that gets in my way!

Joey tried to return to his routine after the night's events, but something had changed within him. The near-death encounter with Tyson and his crew had opened his eyes.

He knew that to ignore the events and continue down the same path of self-destruction would only lead to more misery. If he was ever to rise out of his depression, he needed to understand what had happened to him that night.

How can I get that feeling of peace back?

Joey had an overwhelming sensation that he should find the man that saved him that night. He didn't understand why, but he felt that he was connected to the peace and clarity that he experienced. His rational mind was telling him this was ridiculous – the guy was a gangbanger, not a guardian angel – but his intuitive inner self was pushing him ever forward.

Feeling compelled to find Tyson. Joey overcame his fear and decided to drive to Trentan. He had no idea where to find him, or even how he might react if he did. But he felt he had nothing to lose – his terror in the face of death had once again been replaced by an overriding desire for escape, and after all, Tyson had saved him once. He would trust his gut and take a leap of faith.

As he entered Trentan and made his way through the desolate streets, he started to feel the sense of adrenaline that he had experienced that previous night. He continued to drive nervously through the neighbourhood, getting deeper and deeper into the heart of Trentan. His senses were heightened as he passed pimps, prostitutes and drug dealers on every corner. All was well, until flashing lights and a siren lit his car up from behind. Stomach dropping, Joey began to panic. He knew he was completely out of his depth.

The cops tailed him until he pulled over just before a busy street corner. They got out of their vehicle and walked over to his window. Signalling for him to wind it down.

"What in God's name are *you* doing here, young man?" one of the officers asked sternly. "You know what neighbourhood you're in, right?"

"Are you lost, boy?" The other officer added.

Joey fumbled over his words, remembering the last time he had heard that question. Eventually claiming that he must have taken a wrong turn in his search for Dormanty.

"Well, you're lucky we got to you first," the officer replied as he pointed to a crew of young men on the corner. "That lot would eat you up and spit out the bones if they saw you come through here alone. Do you understand what I'm saying?"

"Yes, sir. Understood, sir," Joey responded in a quivering voice.

After a harsh telling off, the officers eventually let him go. Joey's heart was pounding and sweat was dripping from his brow. He inched away from the kerb and slowly drove off, meeting a red light at the corner just ahead. He was now directly opposite the group of men that the officer was referring to. He nervously turned his head to see if they had noticed him. As he did, he immediately recognised Tyson staring back, a confused look on his face.

Oh shit!

Joey quickly looked ahead and accelerated away.

Tyson couldn't believe his eyes. He looked around at his crew who were completely oblivious to the car that had just rolled past.

"What in the hell is he doing back here?" he mused aloud.

Tyson knew it must have something to do with the other night. He just couldn't figure out why a rich kid would risk coming back to Trentan.

Was he looking for drugs? Surely not. There was no shortage of dealers in the suburbs, nice middle-class university boys that could be trusted not to cut their product with oven cleaner.

The events of that night had already been playing on his mind. Ever since he had let Joey go, he had been questioning his place in the streets. Seeing him again only added fuel to the fire. He immediately took it as a sign. It couldn't be coincidence.

But what did it mean?

Tyson was very intuitive. Living in the present moment allowed him to pick up on guidance from all aspects of life. Be it hunches, coincidences or general gut feelings about situations. In his mind, they were all connected to where he needed to go. Allowing him to successfully navigate through the chaotic street life.

Depending on the guidance, it could direct him to take some sort of necessary action or alternatively just stay patient. Either way, he trusted in it completely. Inevitably, it would always point him in the right direction. Opening up new opportunities, and helping him to avoid danger. In his experience, whenever he didn't follow the direction he would lose out in one way or another. He learned to have complete faith in it and this time was no different.

By the time Joey arrived home, he was a nervous wreck. *What was I thinking? That gangbanger must think I have some kind of death wish.*

After that night, he gave up on the idea of trying to find Tyson. He disregarded it as a foolish decision, one with no real basis. His rational mind had taken over, and was not going to let him follow a hunch that would put him in harm's way again.

So, he began to block it all out and look upon the events that transpired with Tyson as no more than a lucky escape that could have happened to anyone. The experience that followed, the moment of clarity, must have been merely the effects of shock.

That was it for Joey. He was now back at square one. Desperately seeking answers to his mental health struggles and slipping deeper into the grips of addiction, as he tried to numb the pain the only way he knew how. Full bottle, empty glass. That would be reversed soon.

TYSON & JOEY

4

Following the Sign

Tyson knew what he needed to do. He needed to find Joey. There was something about the boy that was necessary for change in his life. That's what intuition was telling him.

He also knew that Joey might simply be a stepping stone to where he really needed to be. In his experience, inner guidance was like a signpost, pointing to a person or place intrinsic to the greater journey.

How am I going to find him? he thought to himself, attempting to decide on his next move. *What do I know about him?*

He didn't even know his name. All he knew was he was white, from the suburbs, and he liked to party in Dormanty.

That was it!

Tyson had met Joey because he and his friends had become lost while looking for a club in Dormanty.

The clubs. That's where I'll find him.

He wouldn't have to scour the suburbs. He could simply wait until Friday night, and take a short walk across town. He had a good feeling about this. He knew Dormanty was the hottest place in town, and was attracting all the rich kids.

If him and his friends are caught up in the party scene, they'll be in Dormanty on a Friday night for sure.

The evening soon arrived, and Tyson was ready to find his man. He was supposed to be out hustling with his crew, but he knew that following his gut instinct was more important. In his place, he had Jimmy take control for the night.

"Where are you going dressed up like that, Ty?" Jimmy asked.

"I'm going to see about a business opportunity," Tyson replied. "You just make sure you hold this corner down until I get back."

"I got this Ty, don't worry about me."

It would be the first time Jimmy was in charge. Tyson was well aware of this, and was apprehensive of how it might play out. Friday nights were often chaotic, especially if the cops decided to come through and sweep the corners for drugs. Tyson knew he had trained his crew well, though, and he trusted Jimmy's judgment.

"I know you do, Jimmy. Trust your instincts out

there," Tyson told his protege, hands firmly clasped on his sholders. After a moment, he left Jimmy on the corner and headed out into the night.

It was a cool, crisp evening, and Tyson was enjoying taking the night off as he causally strolled towards Dormanty. He had to make one quick stop before he got there, though. He was still carrying his gun and needed to stash it. He knew the bars and clubs would have scanners, or a bouncer would single him out thanks to his shaved head and prominent tattoos.

He carried it everywhere in the street. It was a necessary form of protection in his line of work. He rarely had to use it, but at points he would have to bring it out to show a rival dealer he wasn't scared, or threaten a crazed feign. But tonight was different. He couldn't afford an unregistered weapon's charge. That would surely mean jail time, life on the street for his family, and increased difficulty of achieving something of worth in his own future.

As Tyson got closer to Dormanty, he could hear the distant thump of club music and see the bright lights of Main Street illuminating the night sky. He was just a few blocks away at this point, so he located an empty alley and ditched his gun under a dumpster. He initially felt incredibly vulnerable without it, but with every step he took out of Trentan he could feel the hostile energy dissipate. He knew the streets of Dormanty presented no real danger to him.

On the other side of town, Joey and his own crew were getting ready for their night ahead. It was pre-drinks at Sammy's this time. They had the music blasting, and were loading up on a combination of beer and weed before the taxi arrived.

"Are you going to hit this shit?" Craig called out to Joey, holding a blazing joint while he coughed and sputtered.

"Nah man," Joey replied. "I'm cool, that shit makes me paranoid. I'll stick to the beer."

"Really? You used to be all about it. Oh well, more for me."

Joey sank back into the couch and chugged back his eighth beer of the evening.

How can they still enjoy this shit? he wondered. *I can barely taste it. This is a survival mechanism, nothing more.*

"Beep, beep!" sounded the taxi outside.

"Taxi's here boys, get your shit together and let's go!" Sammy yelled, trying to rally up the troops who were in various states of inebriation.

Joey stood up from the couch and sank the remainder

of his beer, crushing the can in his hand and determined to psyche himself up for the night ahead.

"That's the spirit," Manny shouted before slapping him on the rump. "We're going to get some ladies tonight, my friend."

Joey couldn't help but laugh at the situation. The boys were in no form to be picking up. Especially Manny, who was so stoned he could barely open his eyes.

Although he was over the partying and wearisome routine of it all, he appreciated the guys for always including him. Something he tended to overlook in his depressive state.

They made their way outside and clambered into the taxi.

"To Dormanty!" Manny slurred as the car pulled off into the night and began the familiar journey over the bridge.

The taxi pulled up outside Club Premier and the boys spilled out onto the pavement, leaving Joey with the taxi fare. *Usual story.*

"You guys owe me a drink!" he yelled as they stumbled towards the club entrance.

Premier was a trashy joint, the kind where people got loaded at the beginning of a night. The drinks were cheap and the girls even more so. It didn't matter how hammered you were; Premier never kicked anybody out. It was perfect for the guys.

One by one they had their ID's checked and were shuffled into the club. As soon as they got in, they shot off in different directions. Sammy went to the bar for drinks, Craig went to the nearest group of girls and Manny hit the dance floor. Joey had less enthusiasm, so resided to a bar stool where he could sit back, drink and watch the action from a distance.

Not far from Premier, about a block down the main strip, sat Tyson. He was positioned on one of the wooden benches that lined the street. He was taking in the atmosphere, getting a feel for the place and looking out for any sign of Joey and his friends. He knew that hitting every bar would be too hard, and that his best shot of finding them would be to sit back and observe from afar.

Tyson still had no idea what he would do when he found his quarry, but he trusted in his intuition. He knew that meeting Joey was critical to his greater journey; he just didn't know how.

As he sat back on the bench and took it all in, he noticed that there was a large group of people trying to get into a club down the street. No other places had lines at this point in the evening, so it caught his attention.

That's it. Without hesitation, he stood up from the bench and proceeded towards the club.

As he strolled down the street, he could feel his heart beginning to beat faster. Tyson treated the nervous energy as a sign that he was on the right track.

He's in there. I'm sure of it.

Eventually he reached Premier. The line was getting longer by the minute.

I'll be waiting here at least half an hour.

Before committing to the line, he walked past the queue of people until he was at the entrance. He wanted to catch a glimpse inside before lining up. As he peered past the bouncers blocking the door, he heard a voice call out to him.

"Tyson! Is that you, Ty?"

Tyson looked up and recognised his childhood friend Damian staring back at him.

"Damian, my brother!" he responded as he walked up to him and gave him a hug.

He hadn't seen him in years. Damian had left Trentan after getting an athletic scholarship at a university across town.

"Long time, what are you doing here?" Tyson asked.

"I'm working as a bouncer part-time while I study," Damian replied.

Damian got out of Trentan at the right time. He was

running with the same crew as Tyson and would have been consumed by the street life if it wasn't for his athletic ability.

"I'm sorry I haven't been back. I get the family to come see me now," he explained in an apologetic tone.

Tyson understood completely. He knew that Trentan was no place for Damian. He had an opportunity to be successful, and needed to protect it. Coming back to the neighbourhood would be putting it at risk.

"No need to be sorry, brother. I respect what you're doing. You give the people of Trentan hope."

Tyson was proud that his friend had transcended the environment and was on his way to achieving his goals. That's what he wanted as well. To succeed; not only for himself and his family, but also for the greater community of Trentan. Particularly the kids. He wanted to show them that there were other avenues outside of selling drugs and working dead-end jobs.

Tyson saw this as another sign. Bumping into his old friend at the door of the club that he needed to get into was not just a coincidence; it was confirmation that Joey was inside.

"So good to see you my man, it's been way too long. But what the hell are you doing in Dormanty?" Damian said with a chuckle. "This ain't exactly your scene."

"Long story bro, but I'm meeting someone. Matter of fact, he's inside this very club."

"Alright, say no more," Damian replied, presumably assuming that whatever Tyson was up to was illegal. "I trust you to be subtle, Ty – just be careful. I'll catch up with you on your way out."

With that, Tyson shook his hand and proceeded to walk inside the club. The place was packed. He weaved in and out of the crowd, knowing his man would be in there somewhere.

He made his way to the outside courtyard, but there was still no sign. He went back to the edge of the dance floor and scanned the room from afar. He immediately recognised Manny as being one of the guys from that night.

He's close.

He kept searching the room, but there was still no sign of Joey. He made his way over to the bar to find a seat and grab a drink. Keeping a watchful eye on the dance floor as he did.

"Mineral water, please!" he shouted to the barman over the music.

Tyson pulled up a stool and continued to scan the room.

"Rum and coke please," a familiar voice called out

across the bar.

Tyson looked over and immediately recognised the person as Joey.

My man.

Tyson slid from his stool and joined Joey at the other end of the bar. They were now standing side by side. Sipping their drinks and leaning back into the bar, Joey remained oblivious to his new companion.

"Busy night in here," Tyson said, trying to engage small talk.

"Sure is. I can't stand this place," Joey replied, still looking straight ahead.

"So, what's your plans for the night?" Tyson continued.

Joey turned his head to respond, looking him directly in the eye.

What the fuck!

He jumped back instantly, completely startled by Tyson's presence. Tyson immediately reacted by reaching out to shake his hand.

"Tyson. Pleased to finally meet you," he said in a calm manner.

Joey muttered his own name nervously. The two of them stared at each other for a few seconds before Tyson began explaining himself.

"I know you must be surprised to see me tonight. But

let me tell you one thing before I get into why; this is no coincidence. I've been looking for you for the past hour. Ever since I came across you and your friends that night I have been questioning my place in the streets. The old me would have let my brother end you, but I gave you a pass and allowed you to walk away unharmed. I knew something had changed within me after that...

I kept thinking back to that night, and then I saw you again after you were pulled over by the cops in Trentan. I took that as a sign that I needed to find you. This might sound strange, but I figure you are somehow connected to the change I need in my life. I just don't know how."

Joey looked back at Tyson while he explained this, taking a gulp of his rum and coke as he did.

"Wow," he replied. "This is so crazy, I knew there was something bigger to that night too."

"What do you mean by that?" Tyson asked.

"Having a gun to my head and thinking that I was going to be killed completely rattled me," Joey explained. "After you let me go, I ran back to Dormanty, I reckon I was in shock. But what followed was an experience I'll never forget. I think the intensity of that situation forced me into the present moment for the first time in longer than I can remember. After the incident, I walked around Dormanty feeling more alive than I have in years. I was temporarily lifted out of depression. My senses were heightened. Colours became brighter, sounds more distinct, I felt in tune with my reality…and most profound was the feeling of underlying peace. It was like everything was OK for the first time, regardless of what had just happened. I don't know, it's hard to articulate, but I can't stop thinking about it."

Joey took a deep breath before continuing.

"That state didn't last though. It came on quickly, and dissipated as anxiety and depression returned and replaced it. I've been trying to understand what happened ever since. I want to connect to that space again, but I have no idea how."

"So that's what you were doing back in Trentan when I saw you for the second time?" Tyson asked.

"Yeah, I was trying to find you," Joey replied. "It sounds stupid, but I had exactly the same feeling. I felt that I needed to find you in order to understand that peaceful experience."

Joey nervously took another gulp of his rum, before turning to the barman and calling for one more.

"Shall I make it two?" he asked Tyson. "This is some heavy shit for a place like this!"

"No, I'm good. I don't drink," Tyson replied.

Joey was completely rattled by the whole the situation. His anxiety felt through the roof, while Tyson stood across from him completely relaxed.

"I'm sorry man...I'm completely on edge. I'm just trying to understand what's going on here," Joey said.

"Don't be sorry, brother, and don't try and understand what's going on. All I can say is that we have been brought together for a reason, and I think that it's to help one another. I don't know exactly how, but I believe it's necessary for the evolution of both of us."

"Are you some kind of prophet?" Joey replied, half seriously.

Tyson began laughing aloud and grabbed Joey by the shoulder.

"Far from it. In fact, I'm a drug dealer from Trentan. I come from nothing. I live in a social housing building with my mother and little sister. I'm lucky to be alive today, especially as I've seen so many of my friends killed, sent away to prison or get themselves strung out. My reality is harsh, so I don't come to you lightly. I'm deadly serious when I say this shit; this is no joke. I'm supposed to be running a crew on the corner tonight, but I've left that in the hands of my associate to come and find you."

Tyson let his words linger with Joey before continuing.

"One thing I do know, is that I'm completely at peace, though. Underneath all the chaos there is a knowing that everything is OK. A connection to something greater. I think that's what you got a glimpse of that night."

Joey was taken aback by Tyson's words. They hit him right in the chest and made him sit back on his stool. Joey felt embarrassed by his situation when he compared it to Tyson's.

"I'm sorry, man. I didn't realise," he replied, struggling to find an appropriate way to respond.

"Don't be sorry. That's my reality. But like I said, I'm at peace and that's something you can't buy. This peace has come out of the chaos, forged through my time on the streets. Out of adversity I have found the truth behind it all, and with that you not only end your personal suffering but you can do and achieve anything."

There was a brief silence before Tyson and Joey were joined by the rest of the boys. Sammy, Manny and Craig came up to Joey and started talking girls, completely oblivious of Tyson standing right next to him.

"Who's your friend?" Sammy eventually asked Joey.

Joey stumbled over his words before Tyson took the cue to introduce himself.

"The name's Tyson."

"You look familiar. Did you go to Fitzroy High?" Sammy asked.

Tyson laughed, quite amused by the fact that the boys had no idea that he was part of the crew that they had encountered a few weeks back.

"Must be someone else you're thinking of, I think I have one of those faces," he replied. "Anyway boys, I was just leaving. Enjoy the rest of your night."

"You're off? So what happens next?" Joey asked as Tyson began to leave.

"Come over here," Tyson said, indicating him to join him in private away from his friends.

"This is just the beginning Joey, we had to meet. That's all that tonight was about. Now we've done so, we can begin to reveal why we truly have been brought together. You just have to trust that we were destined to be brothers. Trust in the bigger picture. That our two worlds collided for a reason, and it has something to do with the peace you seek and the change I need."

Joey said nothing.

"I'm busy this week, but next Sunday I want you to meet me for lunch at Joe's cafe on the Dormanty waterfront. We'll go from there. Are you with me? Sunday at noon?" Tyson pressed.

Joey nodded in agreement, "I'll be there."

"My man."

With that, Tyson turned and walked out of the club.

He had left a strong impression on Joey. Tyson had a calm about him, and his words resonated with truth. Joey knew he had to meet him again.

TYSON & JOEY

5

Lunch

Joey awoke early on the Sunday morning in question, apprehensive about meeting Tyson. It had been over a week since they had spoken, and Joey found himself wondering if the other man would even turn up; they hadn't exchanged numbers, so he had no way of confirming their appointment. Anxiety playing all kinds of scenarios over in his mind, Joey started to worry that it might be some kind of set up; that Tyson was luring him into a trap. Deep down, however, he knew that Tyson was genuine, and had something important to teach him. He just wished he knew what.

Across town, Tyson was rising out of bed late. Saturday night was always busy, so he had been working until the early hours of the morning. He was well aware that he was meeting Joey at noon. However, unlike Joey, he didn't feel any nerves about their connection. He knew that it was part of something bigger, and was critical to both their lives.

Their lives could not have been more different. Joey

grew up in the affluent northern suburbs, and was now attending university. Tyson was raised on the violent streets of Trentan, and was now a prominent drug pusher. Although from different worlds, the common ground was that they were both at critical points. Tyson needed change, as it was only a matter of time before the streets consumed him. Joey needed peace. Something his depression was robbing him of.

Tyson knew that he could help Joey with this quest; after all, he had found peace amidst the chaos of his own life. To stay alive and succeed on the streets, he had developed his own code to live by. One based on the core principal of giving himself fully to the present moment. No matter how harsh his reality was, he would not turn away from it. He would always look it directly in the eye. By living this way, he unknowingly tapped into something far greater. Through presence, he found inner harmony. He knew connecting to this space was the ultimate truth in life, and that everything else was secondary.

It was 11.45am, and Joey was already waiting in Joe's Cafe on Dormanty waterfront. It was a beautiful day, so he decided to grab a seat in the al fresco dining area that overlooked the river. Joey sat there nervously, trying to take his mind off things by reading the morning news. *Another murder in Trentan*, he read on the front page. This only heightened his anxiety. He was considering whether he should even wait around. Suddenly, that paranoia that it might be some sort of trap returned, and he stood with the intention of leaving. His rational mind was telling him that this meeting was a bad idea. That meeting with a drug dealer from Trentan could only end one way. But as he began to walk off, Tyson appeared in front of him.

"Joey? Looks like I just got here in time."

"I was just going to the bathroom," he responded, stumbling over his words as he tried to gather his composure.

"No problem, I'll grab us a seat and see you back here. Do you want a drink?" Tyson asked as Joey nervously took himself off to toilet even though he didn't need to go.

"Ahhh...orange juice, please," he replied as he walked off. It was the first time he had ordered a soft drink in Dormanty for some time.

Get yourself together, he thought to himself as he splashed his face with water before returning to the table. When he returned, Tyson was sitting back in his chair admiring the river views. "Beautiful out here, isn't it?"

Joey began to relax in Tyson's presence. His calm nature eased his anxiety.

They both proceeded to order food, and chat away

like old friends. Talking sport, family and girls. Tyson knew Joey was nervous, so he wanted to make him feel comfortable before getting into the real reason why they were together on this sunny afternoon. Once they had finished their meals and covered every possible topic of small talk, Tyson began shifting the conversation.

"So how are you feeling, Joey? You mentioned last time that you had been struggling with depression."

Joey was surprised by the question. No one ever asked him how he was feeling. He looked away and contemplated things for a minute. Before long, it all came flooding out.

"I don't know, man. I can't seem to get out of this mind state. It's awful. It completely saps the energy out of me, and nothing seems to offer me any sense of enjoyment or pleasure anymore. I feel guilty about feeling this way. I'm well aware that my life situation is good. I come from a privileged background and am afforded many opportunities, but even that seems meaningless. I feel completely empty inside, and there is an overwhelming sense of hopelessness. No matter what I do, I can't break out of it. At my worst, I don't want to live anymore. I find a sense of relief in the thought that I will die some day, and will finally be free from this mental suffering. I just don't have the balls to take my own life, otherwise I probably would have."

Joey took a deep breath before continuing. "That's how I'm feeling on a daily basis. I know that must sound like a cry from an ungrateful rich kid, but if I'm completely honest that's what I'm dealing with and I'm desperately trying to find some answers. I've tried everything; medication, therapy, different self-help remedies. Nothing gets to the core of the problem. They only mask it temporarily, and give a false sense of hope. The only relief I have had from it was the experience after we meet for the first time. Like I said last time, that experience shocked me into a blissful state of present moment awareness, where I temporarily forgot all about the depression."

"That's it," Tyson replied back. "Forget about the story that you just told me. Don't focus on the idea that you are depressed and are desperately trying to break out of it. By doing that, all you are doing is becoming identified with it, and once you're identified with it you become a prisoner to it."

Tyson looked Joey intently in the eyes as he explained further.

"First off, stop telling that story. To yourself, and to other people. That is only perpetuating your feelings. The more you identify with it, the worse it will get. Secondly, you already have the answer to end your suffering. You mentioned it in your account."

"What's that?" Joey responded back.

"Present moment awareness," Tyson said. "That's the key. You touched it briefly, as you mentioned. Anyone can touch it briefly, though; it's being able to stay connected to that conscious space that's the challenge. That's the only place you will ever find peace in this world, no matter what your life situation. Making the present moment the foundation of your life is the ultimate truth."

Tyson let his words sit with Joey for a minute.

"I can teach you how to end your anguish. But you have to stay committed to the teachings if you ever want to free yourself. It will take perseverance, and absolute trust in the process. Know this though, Joey; I'm not giving you anything you don't already have. Peace is not something you *find*. It already exists within you. You are simply uncovering it, and reconnecting with it. It is a shift from a mind-orientated state of living in this world to state of being and presence. A state beyond thought. As you enter this space, you detach from your mind and expose it as being the true cause of your suffering."

Tyson's words resonated deeply with Joey. He had never looked at his issues as being a product of the mind, and never knew that there was another state of being that existed beyond thought. He always thought that he was *defined* by his mind; that the endless stream of thoughts that narrated every aspect of his life, for good or for bad, were who he was. Tyson was proposing this was untrue. It was difficult for Joey to comprehend.

"Trust me, Joey. Look at me. Do you see worry or concern on my face? I'm at peace with this world. I'm at peace with life and death, and the chaotic environment that I come from. I found this peace through the present moment, and with my guidance, you will too. Not only will you become free from your mental torment, but life will open up to you in ways you never imagined."

"But how can you know all this, and still choose to live the life that you do? If life opens up to you through this state of being, then why are you still in Trentan?" Joey asked.

"That's a very good question," Tyson replied. "I ask myself the same thing all the time. All I know is, the universe works in mysterious ways. I have trust and faith that change will come into my life when it's supposed to. And out of that, the life that I want for my family and myself *will* manifest. Until that time, I accept, and remain present to my current environment. I don't try to escape it through temporary measures. I give myself fully to the *now*, and wait for the intuitive guidance. That's what led me to you."

Joey was intrigued by Tyson's words. "So how can I pay you? What do you get out of this?" Joey responded back.

"I don't want your payment, Joey. I'm here to teach you, and that is all. Whatever benefit I experience from it will clarify in time. That's not important. What's important is me passing on this knowledge, so you can end your personal suffering and find some peace."

"I'm in!" Joey responded eagerly. "When do we start?"

"Right here, right now," Tyson replied without hesitation. "*Here* and *now* is the beginning of your teaching. Look around and what do you see? People walking. Cars driving by. Boats on the river. Am I right?"

"Yes, I see all those things," Joey replied.

"Now what do you hear? People talking, cars moving, birds chirping and aeroplanes overhead amongst other things. How about taste? I'm guessing pancakes and maple syrup, with a hint of orange from the juice?"

Tyson explained that these were all just sensory observations, picked up by sight, hearing and taste. The labels that we apply to them are unimportant. He explained to Joey that he needed to look past the labels and just see, hear, taste and smell things for what they are. This was the way to connect with them in their fullest, and in doing so, enter the present moment.

"Now, what do you feel?" Tyson asked.

"All sorts of things. The chair pushing into my skin. The heat of the sun. The sweat dripping down my brow,"

Joey replied.

"Exactly. All these things create a different sensation. Whether its heat from the sun or a cold chill in winter, each affects the body in a different way, creating a different physical feeling. Then there are your thoughts and emotions. You've been feeling depressed, meaning your energy is very low, and all other emotions are buried underneath. You're also feeling anxious, a constant sensation of unease and unnecessary worry and fear about the future. These are your predominant feelings at the moment. What creates these feelings you may ask? Why, when your life situation is seemingly so good, do you feel this way? It starts with the mind. When you're identified with your mind, which you are, then your emotions become a direct product of the myriad of thoughts that are streaming through your head at any given moment.

In your case, these thoughts have become increasingly negative, as they do with a lot of people. When you identify and believe in these thoughts, they create negative emotions that match. First, you may experience episodes of anxiety, then that can lead you into a depressive state. So, the catalyst for it all is your thoughts and your identification with them. Are you following me?"

"I am," replied Joey, nodding his head. "So, it's simply a matter of changing my thoughts?"

"It might appear that way, but that's not the case.

What we want to do is *dis-identify* with our thoughts completely. Which means to dis-identify with the *mind*. You want to bring yourself out of thought, and into the present moment. Let the thoughts come and go without identifying with them. You simply stay focussed on what is happening at this very moment, using your sense perceptions to anchor you. See, hear, taste, smell and feel the very essence of your reality. This process takes you out of thought and into the *now*. The only thing that's real.

Now, go deeper. Focus on your inner body and feel the life within you. Start by concentrating on one part of the body, like your hands or feet. Put all your attention there, and begin to feel the internal energy field. In time, you will be able to feel it throughout your entire body. You should feel a deep peace while you do this. You are connecting with consciousness in its formless state. The un-manifested. All these techniques will bring you deeper into the present moment, and begin to dissolve your anxiety."

"Wow! I certainly feel a heightened sense of positivity about me. But I can feel it fading as my thoughts take over again," Joey responded.

"That's just a glimpse, brother. Imagine having that as your constant state of being. That's what enlightenment is."

Presence - The Foundation of Everything

Tyson paused for a moment, and peered into his audience. They remained captivated, which was a relief; not only were they following the very point of his lecture, but it ensured that they would fully absorb his next teaching.

"I have come to understand that the practical application of presence is fundamental to everything," he explained. "It is the foundation to a fulfilled life, and connects you to a state of inner peace. If you are to develop one thing in life, it *has* to be presence.

The beautiful thing is, anybody and everybody can access this state of being and its amazing power. No matter what your current life situation is, whether perceived as positive or negative by the mind, bringing yourself out of thought and into the present moment can only benefit it.

The simple idea that the present moment is all you ever have is life-changing when you truly understand it. All you have is *right now*; there is no past or future. There is only your experience of the moment. The past was experienced in the *now*, and so will the future. Therefore, it makes you question why we place so much emphasis on that what has happened, or what may or may not occur? Many people I come into contact with are living predominantly in the past or future, completely forgetting about the *now*. It's always about the next thing, or time spent dwelling over past events. The present moment becomes redundant in this way of living.

When you are engaged with the present, life begins working for *you*. You become connected to your reality, and instinctively know what action needs to be taken. You let the present moment guide you, responding only to the givens of the situation without being distracted by the mind.

There are examples of this everywhere. Take an athlete in a sport like basketball. When the athlete is in the zone, meaning completely present with no distractions, he or she can't miss. Every shot is organic and precise, and in complete harmony with the moment.

When someone is not distracted by their mind and obsessive thought patterns, they can truly engage with the task in front of them – no matter what it is. This allows them to perform at a high level, and produce the results needed for the givens of a situation. An athlete will excel, an artist will unleash creativity, and a spouse will have the clarity to see what their significant other needs. These are just a few examples, but the point I'm trying to make is that this way of being applies to every aspect of your life. No exceptions.

When you truly live in the moment, past and future do not exist. You lose yourself to the *now*. Situations from all facets of life offer glimpses into this space. In an instant, you can be taken out of thought and plunged into the *now*. For example, a joke can cause you to be overcome with laughter. In that moment, you are not thinking about the past or future; you are simply enjoying the joke. An extreme example could be a car accident. People often say these experiences cause time to slow down. In such a case, you are shocked by the intensity of the situation into the present moment to the point that your mind's understanding of linear time is altered.

The sad reality is, the majority of people only experience this state of presence when they are forced into it by an external event. But imagine if you could spend your day walking around like that. Feeling completely connected to your surroundings, with no regret of the past or worry of the future, only engaged with the *now*. Imagine what that would do to your life.

The quality of your future depends completely on the quality of your present. When the present moment becomes the foundation of your life, the life you truly desire on a deep level will begin to manifest effortlessly. Once you take care of the internal, the external will look after itself. It's incredibly simple, but at the same time so difficult to truly grasp and stick to. However, if you can, you will be astounded at how your life begins to transform.

I'm not a religious man, but many prominent prophets and spiritual leaders have preached this same message. Jesus said, "seek the Kingdom of God first, and his righteousness and all these things shall be added unto you." He referred to the Kingdom as being inside of you, inside *all* of us, and that once that has become the primary focus in one's life, the other things on the material plane will come effortlessly. It's the peace within; the consciousness and the stillness, which so many have pointed to. Buddha taught through his teachings that we should not dwell in the past, nor dream of the future, but concentrate the mind solely on the present.

This conscious space is described as Nirvana in Buddhism, Christ Consciousness in Christianity, Taqwa in Islam and Samadhi in Yoga. It's the state of enlightenment that so many are seeking, many of whom are unaware of its true nature. This space is not something you find; it's something you *connect* with. It's within all of us, and the portal is through the present moment. It is not a mystical, hard-to-reach place that only the select few have access to. It is available to everyone, and its simplicity and true power are unmistakable once realised.

Of course, the question remains, how do we bring ourselves out of thought when we are so identified with our mind? It's a process, and the present state will not come to you without some pain. You have to dis-identify from your thoughts, which many of us find ourselves addicted to. You will need to have absolute trust and faith in the process, especially if you are defining your sense of self through them. You'll need to step back, and see the thoughts for what they are – fiction. Not real. From here, you will start to engage with the real you, the conscious space beyond the mind."

Pausing for a breath, Tyson then began discussing the next topic on his agenda.

A way out of Suffering

"No one emotion lasts forever – unless you resist it. Just like everything else in this world, our feelings are fleeting. They come and go. You need to embrace your emotions and let them run their course, no matter how painful they are. If accepted fully, they will soon lift and reveal a lesson or truth about their cause. Your emotions are trying to teach you something. There is always a message behind them; something that cannot be analysed on the surface of thought, and only becomes clear when accepted.

Trust the pain in your life, and know that it is trying to teach you something. Do not fight or distract yourself from it. You are only temporarily relieving it, and it *will* come back stronger. Bringing presence into your life is the first step. Take it slowly at first. Think of it as a process, whereby little by little you are strengthening its foundation. This will not be easy; in fact, it will be painful working through weighty emotions. Know this, however; every time you practice, and fully accept and sit with the pain, you are elevating your degree of consciousness and improving the quality of your life.

In the beginning, the mind will resist. It will create excuses for you not to stay in the moment, and indulge in the relentless streams of thought. You must have the will power to resist this impulse. It may take every ounce of your strength to not be drawn back into the negative story in your head. Every time you successfully do this, however, and truly sit with your feelings and thoughts without reacting, you are gaining greater control over your mind. Through this process, anxiety and depression will begin to dissolve. One day at a time, one situation at a time, one moment at a time.

Each time you practice presence, you are rising out of mental suffering. Don't just accept what I'm saying; try it for yourself. Give yourself fully to the present moment while experiencing an episode of anxiety. Simply observe your thoughts and emotions, without engaging with them. You will notice that when the intensity of them subsides, a sense of peace will flood through you. This is you leaving suffering behind.

Everyone is at different levels. Some people are in severe states of depression, to the point that leaving their bed is a struggle. Their energy levels are so low that they can barely muster the strength to care for themselves, let alone hold down a job or engage socially. Others suffer from episodes of extreme anxiety, followed by brief periods of depression where they are low for a spell then come out of it and are back to their 'normal' selves – whatever that means. There are different levels, different degrees of mental illness. But irrespective, no matter what level you find yourself at, the process of leaving suffering behind and living a life of peace and fulfilment is always the same.

Often, when people feel negative emotions approaching, they become afraid and try to avoid them by any means possible. This is completely understandable, as they contain a feeling of hopelessness. One that terrifies them, and offers no light. Naturally, they want to escape. That's why things like drugs, alcohol and prescription medicine are so appealing. They numb you temporarily, so you don't have to deal with the reality of the *now*. In the long run, alas, this only makes things worse. Every time you block or distract yourself from these feelings, they come back more intensified the next time. This fuels the addictive cycle in the process. To avoid this vicious cycle, you have to embrace the mental suffering. Do not turn away from it. It won't kill you.

Presence is critical to this process. It enables you to be conscious of the cause of your suffering, and allows you to sit with the pain. Consciousness is light. You are shining light on your suffering and taking away its power. You are revealing it for what it is. An illusion created by the very mind that you have come to identify with so closely.

Ultimately all you are doing is detaching yourself from the story in your head and focussing your attention on the *here* and the *now*. It's a simple process, but it involves a great deal of trust and faith. I know this, because I live exclusively in the *here* and the *now*. Always and forever, I give myself to the present moment. I practice what I preach.

I don't see my words as being profound, and I don't want you to hang onto to them as though they are. They are simply signposts, asking you to look inside and see for yourselves what the cause of your suffering is. The pain and adversity that *I* experienced connected me with the peace within, so stop analysing your life situation. It's secondary to what is happening within. Take yourself out of thought and into the stillness of the *now*. That's your starting point; that's the only place you will find any peace, and begin to rise out of the suffering that your mind is creating."

Tyson may not have seen his own words as profound,

but it was fair to say that he was in a minority. Hundreds of eyes were locked onto his as he returned to explaining the nature of his friendship with Joey.

6

The Beach

Tyson was out until the early hours of the morning, managing his dealers across Trentan. He only managed to snatch a few hours of sleep, but he was conditioned for it. Being tired was part of the game. Once up, he made sure his mother and sister were taken care of before making his way to the station. Flaxton Beach was to be his destination, and as luck would have it, it was the final station on the line. He had politely but forcefully declined Joey's offer of a lift as he enjoyed the train journey, especially when he didn't have to worry about falling asleep and missing his stop. It was about an hour's ride to the coast, cutting through industrial districts and neighbourhoods similar to Trentan.

On the other side of town, Joey was nervous and excited about meeting Tyson again. He had been up late into the night mulling over his words. It wasn't until he became still and simply concentrated on his breathing that he began to understand what he was saying at a deeper level. He observed that, when he stepped back from his mind and let his thoughts come and go without engaging, stillness and peace would follow.

This gave Joey hope. Anxiety and depression had consumed him for months, so to finally have a glimpse of light felt like a blessing. He left early for the beach, allowing himself an hour and a half for the journey in case of traffic. He crossed the bridge into Dormanty and, like the train, followed the river edge to the coastline. It was a beautiful day, and he was looking forward to seeing the ocean. It occurred to Joey that, as he had grown older, he had stopped visiting the beach. Perhaps that was something he would have to rectify.

Tyson woke to the sound of the train conductor announcing, "now approaching Flaxton Beach, where this train terminates," over the loud speaker. Still groggy, he made his way out of the carriage and onto the platform. From there, it was only a short walk down to the beach.

At the same time, Joey was pulling into the main car park, which sat at the other end of the beach. Composing himself, he got out of the car and made his way along the boardwalk in the direction of the station. He still got very nervous before meeting his new mentor. It was not every that he hung out with a drug dealer. Tyson did the same and began walking towards the carpark.

"Yo!" Joey said aloud as he spotted Tyson in the distance.

"Howsit bro," Tyson said tiredly as they walked up and embraced. "Just woke up, crashed out for the entire train ride. What's been happening?"

"I'm good," Joey replied, "feeling much better. I had a long night going over what you said, trying to understand it all. After stressing myself out, I simply followed my breathing and became still. It was only then that I felt the peace that you refer to."

"That's good, Joey. This truth cannot be understood at the level of *thought*; only once it's been put into practice." Tyson replied. "I, on the other hand, had a long night serving cracked out feigns. Never get addicted to drugs, Joey. Don't even try to beat them – *they will win*. I've seen it destroy my community. I'm part of the problem, I know, but in my defence, it would still be there if you took me away. It's one of the main vices that people turn to when trying to escape their reality. Addiction applies to everything though. It even applies to your thoughts, did you know that?"

Addicted to Thinking

Once again, Tyson assumed the body language and tone of a lecturer, ready to share his knowledge and experience with the paying customers of his talk.

"Many of us are addicted to thinking, constantly

mulling over the thoughts in our head. Dwelling on the past, or worrying about the future. We have a strong compulsion to do this, and we end up driving ourselves crazy in the process. We can't stop it. We feel that we *have* to think in order to survive. That if we don't, our life will spin out of control. The impulse to think can be incredibly strong, particularly if you're identified with your mind, which most people are. When you become present and watch your thoughts without engaging, you will really begin to appreciate this. You will clearly see and feel the addiction trying to draw you back into thought.

The impulse to engage in thinking is simply your addiction to it. Like an addict, you need a fix to satisfy the craving. When you first practice presence, you will notice that your thoughts are highly energised and have strong pull to take you out of the *now*. This pull is the addiction. As you continue to practice, and become less identified with your mind, you will find that the pull weakens, and eventually breaks. Just like any other addiction, if you resist the urge to use, the stronghold will wane.

Nevertheless, just like an addict, you will relapse from time to time. These old, conditioned patterns of thinking will rear their head and suck you back into the chaos. Don't let these lapses deter you. Simply *recognise* that you are still identified with your mind, and keep practicing presence.

Now, don't make the mistake of thinking that I wander through life empty-headed. Thoughts are always there in the background, narrating every aspect of my life, and depending on my current life situation, they may be positive or negative. What is not there is the urge to *engage* in this type of thinking. I know that it can only lead to sadness. More importantly, I know that nothing meaningful can be achieved through it. The true magic lies behind thought in the stillness, so that's where I keep myself. Like that day at the beach, for example. I just enjoyed the scenery. Breathed in the fresh air, and turned my face to feel the warmth of the sun. I absorbed my senses fully in the moment.

That doesn't change the fact that all I've done tonight is talk, though. The practical application of presence is key. You must be self-disciplined, and practise it at every opportunity you can. This will bring you out of thought and into the *now*. Meditation is a fine way to do this, as one of the most direct ways of bringing yourself into the present moment."

Meditation

"Consistent meditation builds upon the foundation of presence in your life. You carry this conscious state from the session into the rest of your day. It's such a simple practice, yet so few people do it. All it takes is a few minutes a day, depending on how deep you want to go. It requires some patience in the beginning, but you can find your own rhythm in the way you practice. There's no one size fits all when it comes to meditation; some people follow their breathing, others hum prayer or a mantra, and others achieve presence through a more physical realm like Yoga. The thing is, there is no correct way to meditate, any more than there is a correct way to breathe. There will only be a way that feels most comfortable for you.

Myself, I simply follow my breathing. Bringing my awareness to the air coming in and out of my lungs. I then bring my awareness to the sounds around me, whatever they may be, and at points begin to feel the various sensations throughout my body. I use all of my senses to bring me into the present moment and into a meditative state, a state of absolute presence. That's all meditation is; a practice that brings you into the present moment, and allows you to stay there for a period of time.

The rewards for such a simple exercise are incredible. By becoming more connected to the *now* and bringing that into your day, you reduce stress and improve your overall health in the process.

Contrary to popular belief, meditation is not just a spiritual endeavour, as science is beginning to embrace the practice as well. Studies have shown that, through mediation, you strengthen the connections between the left and right sides of your brain, increasing grey matter and enhancing brain functionality.

To access its true power, you must be consistent with it. Ideally, discipline yourself to meditate every day, even if only for a few minutes. Soon it won't feel like a chore anymore. It will become a practice that you embrace, and wish to share with others. Just don't allow it be your only practice; that's a common mistake. It cannot be relied on solely. Being present should apply to all aspects of your life. Everyday jobs can also be used to bring you into a meditative state, and into present moment. Even the most mundane and dull of tasks, such as hoovering or washing dishes.

Ultimately, the more you can consistently bring yourself out of thought and into the moment the better. As you do so, your identification with your mind is being broken. No longer will you react to your thoughts and emotions, and create anguish. You will have the ability to simply step back and let these sensations wash over you."

Tyson and Joey continued to walk along the boardwalk and talk through the teachings.

"Alright that's enough Joey, too much talking," Tyson said mid conservation. "I'm going for a swim man. There's no way I'm coming all the way out here and not getting in the ocean. Look at it – its beautiful." Tyson pointed at the glistening blue-green water. "This is all that matters Joey, this moment. *Here* and *now* – nothing more nothing less."

And with that, Tyson stripped down to his pair of shorts and made a dash for the water. Faster and faster he ran towards the shoreline, diving in when he reached its edge. Clearly excited to be there.

I want to be like that, Joey found himself contemplating as he watched from a distance. *I want to find that joy in the simple pleasures of life, liberated of concerns of what others thought of him.*

As he contemplated, he found himself dredging up memories from his childhood. He remembered coming to the beach with his father and playing without a care in the world. No worry for the past or threat for the future. As he watched Tyson simply enjoy, it reminded him of that childlike state.

Maybe the present moment re-connects you with the joy you naturally experience as a child?

"Don't think…. just be," he said aloud as he sat down on the sand and lit a cigarette. He was clearly struggling to enjoy the moment like Tyson, but was aware that the overthinking was not helping.

Tyson laid on his back and floated along the shoreline, noticeably in a different state from Joey. To him, being at the beach was a place of solitude. It briefly took him away from the harshness of his reality in Trentan. All his stress and tension was carried away by the soft rocking waves of the ocean, tossed and disregarded like the discarded rubbish that had been cast into the sea.

This is paradise.

TYSON & JOEY

7

Shift in Consciousness

"Alright. I'm changing tack again. I have another outtake of Joey's journal, which he has given me permission to share tonight. The point of reading this entry is to really hit home the importance of patience. It's essential if you are ever going to make lasting changes and leave mental suffering behind. Ok, here we go." Tyson said, as he sat down on the stool and began to read.

"Whenever I feel anxiety rising within me, I know exactly what I must do. I must take a deep breath and become present. Focusing solely on the reality before me, and detaching from the endless streams of thought running through my mind. I know these are the cause of my anxiety.

Unfortunately, sometimes, I'm not strong enough. Sometimes the thoughts draw me back in and I can't stay present. I have to engage with them. When this happens, I am temporarily sucked back into extreme anxiety that is connected to them. In these moments, I forget completely about Tyson's teachings. Today was such an experience.

I was at university and went to hand in an assignment which was late by half an hour. The lecturer had already left, so I couldn't give it to her until the next morning.

Instantly, I was overcome by panic. My mind went into overdrive, thinking up the worst possible scenarios. *You're going to fail, and will never graduate* – that was all my brain would allow me to think. Anxiety consumed me. My chest tightened, my palms became sweaty and my heart began to race.

Fuck Joey! What do I do?

I began running around the campus like a mad man, trying to track down the lecturer. Running in and out of classrooms and even checking the staff parking lot. I was completely flustered, not knowing what to do next.

Where the fuck is she!

I couldn't take it anymore, I needed to relieve the anxiety, whatever it took. So I ducked into a convenience store and grabbed a pack of smokes. *Instant relief,* as I dragged hard back on a cigarette and let the nicotine temporarily take away the stress. I was calm again. That was when I remembered Tyson's teachings.

You're stronger than this Joey. Do not let the anxiety control you.

In that moment, I dropped the cigarette and simply breathed, focusing only on the air coming in and out of my lungs. I started to engage with all my senses, observing my surroundings, and brought myself fully into the present moment.

The panic subsided, and I was back. I realised instantly what had happened; I had engaged with my old patterns of thinking. The root cause of my anxiety.

At least I have perspective now, and see where I'm failing.

I know that when the initial panic sets in, I need to bring myself into the *now*. Only then will I have clarity about the situation and make the right decision. In this case, there was nothing I could do. The lecturer had gone home, so regardless, I could not hand in the assignment. Me running around like a crazy person did nothing to change that fact.

So, it's a process, and I'm still trying to break through this cycle of anxiety. But I'm aware of it now. I know what the triggers are, and know how to deal with them when they arise. But like today, I also know I may not be able to stay present. When it comes on strong, sometimes I cannot help but be sucked in.

I call that a relapse, and part of my road to recovery. Today I relapsed into anxiety. But I won't let that deter me. I recognise that I wasn't conscious enough, and know that I will be stronger next time."

"That's an important entry," Tyson stated to the audience after closing the journal. "It highlights the process of rising above mental suffering. There will be setbacks along the way, where you slip into the old states of anxiety-driven thinking, just as Joey described. However, they should never dishearten you. They are simply wake up calls; reminders that you still have work to do. Do not ignore them, as you will quickly slip back into the old patterns more regularly. Acknowledge that you were not strong enough to stay present, just as Joey did, and continue to practice so you are more prepared the next time around.

Ok, let me continue with the story. I'll try stay on track and stop going off on tangents. Unless I think it's absolutely necessary. Where was I? That's right, Joey was starting to consistently apply the teachings." Tyson delved back into his narrative.

Joey tried to get through the next week at university while applying Tyson's teachings, but he was struggling to cope, feeling as though he was on the verge of breaking down. The practices were liberating, but terrifying at the same time. He knew he had to detach from his mind, but at the same time knew his whole identity was conceptualised through it. To fully embrace Tyson's teachings would mean letting go completely.

He drove home in silence late one evening after studying. He would usually have the radio playing, but he wanted to absorb Tyson's words. Joey could feel he was on the verge of change as the truth began to sink in.

Once home, he felt his anxiety coming on strong. He found himself mulling over all the negative thoughts that streamed through his mind, unable to stay present. He was completely confused about what was happening to him. Why had he dropped even lower after discovering the answer to his suffering?

One step forward, two steps back, he thought to himself darkly.

Exhausted and frustrated, he sat in his courtyard, chain-smoking. Complete darkness overcame him as he dragged back the last inch of a cigarette. He thought of his old friends, from what felt like his old life. Sammy had grown frustrated with him, accusing him of joining a cult and 'preaching hippy bullshit' when Joey attempted to explain why he had lost interest in drinking and nightclubs. Manny had laughed in his face when he suggested they meditate together.

Then, without warning, he was overcome by a deep joy from within. He stood and began bouncing on the spot, as the feeling flooded his body. In that moment, he was overcome with absolute clarity. A sudden shift in consciousness forced him into the present moment and separated him from the negative story in his head.

Tyson's truth resonated within and lifted him out of his

maudlin state. He stood there, listening to the negative self-talk without engaging with it. He let it wash over him. There was now a knowing that it was not based in reality. The mind was creating a story that he had been identifying with. This was the cause of his suffering, not the situation itself.

He recognised there were two incarnation of himself, but only one was real. There was his mind, the myriad of thoughts narrating every aspect of his life. Then there was consciousness, the stillness behind thought. These two parts became very clear that night. He knew consciousness was the answer.

This sudden realisation caused all Joey's anxiety to dissolve. The cloud of darkness lifted, and he was connected with the peace underneath. Tyson's words had finally sunk in.

From that point a new way of being emerged within Joey. He was now *present*. Connected to his surroundings, and engaged with the reality in front of him. He knew that to remain in this state, he would need to continue to practice presence, and not allow the mind to draw him back into thought. It was now clear that his thoughts had been telling him a negative narrative that only strengthened if he played into it. By watching them and not reacting, he now had control over his mind, and the anxiety and depression that was so intrinsically connected to it.

Finally, he had found the solution to the mental torment that had haunted him for years. *Presence*. So simple, but so easy to overlook. That evening's suffering had forced him into the present moment. Tyson's words had acted like a catalyst, aiding the shift in consciousness. Seeds of truth that resonated when all hope seemed lost.

As he began to walk around in this renewed state, his whole world began to change. Not only had the mental suffering departed, but he also felt a genuine connection to his surroundings. As a result, his conversations with people were more engaging. He was more focussed at university, and found himself to be much sharper in everyday tasks.

As Tyson had suggested, he used everyday tasks to help him stay present. He would focus all his attention on what he was doing, even with the most mundane chores. This trained him to always stay in the moment, and not drift back into destructive thought patterns.

In the past, he had no sense of presence and was living exclusively through his mind. Hence, when negative patterns of thinking came along, Joey would believe in them whole-heartedly. This would drive up the anxiety and eventually bring on a bout of depression, a vicious cycle that had been getting worse with every episode. From this present state, he was now able to break the cycle.

8

Trentan

Two weeks had passed when Joey received a call from Tyson. He proposed to meet in Trentan. Tyson assured him that he would be fine, aware that it was particularly unsafe for out-of-towners. Joey agreed to meet, though he remained somewhat apprehensive about what Tyson had planned. At the same time, he had been through massive changes since seeing his friend and mentor last, and he was excited to share his progress. He knew he still had much to learn, but the critical shift in consciousness had already happened. It was now about the continual practice of this new way of being. He was curious about what Tyson still had to teach him.

The following day Joey made the trip to Trentan, meeting Tyson in a local diner not far from his building.

"Joey! How are you, brother?" Tyson asked as Joey joined him at his table.

"I'm good, man. Couldn't be better, in fact. I've been through a lot of changes in the past two weeks. After

I left you, I started putting your words into practice. Trying to stay present in my everyday tasks and detach from my thoughts. It was as though the mind resisted and became stronger, causing me to experience intense episodes of anxiety – and that plunged me into an even deeper depressive state. I felt like I had hit rock bottom. I was completely confused, as I was applying exactly what you taught me. I guess that wasn't enough. I had to let that truth transform me at a deeper level. Out of that very low point, a deep realisation came over me. It was as though you had planted the seeds, and they just needed time to grow.

I grew to understand the two different Joeys, as crazy as that sounds. Consciousness, and the mind. In that moment, I was forced into consciousness and was able to step back and watch my thoughts from a distance. I became separated from my mind, and detached from the negative story in my head. I knew from that moment on that presence was the answer. That night, I gave myself fully to the *now* and was instantly elevated out of the mental suffering into a peaceful state. This is where I am now. Conscious, connected to the *here* and the *now*, and able to watch the mind from a distance without engaging. I finally feel free from the anxiety and depression."

Tyson sat back in his chair putting his hands behind his head and smiled. "I'm glad, brother. The shift has happened. You're now aware of your own torment, and can bring that presence into every aspect of your life. It's a beautiful thing, rising out of thought and becoming connected to your reality. You will notice your world begin to transform. Like I said, once you take care of the internal, the external will begin to change. This change will happen down to the finest details with regards to the situations and people you attract into your life."

"So, you believe in that whole concept that you attract what you put out?" Joey asked.

"Absolutely. The law of attraction is a real concept. Like it or not, you are attracting the very situations that you are experiencing," Tyson replied.

Attraction

"The law of attraction is a real thing, and is obvious when you look at your life situation, or that of people around you," Tyson explained to his audience. "You attract the energy that you are putting out. If you're putting out aggressive energy, you will attract aggressive situations – like attracts like. For the majority of people, they are attracting by default. Enticing situations which match the story in their head, which is often conditioned negative patterns of thinking.

From this perspective, if you put yourself in a positive state by blocking or changing negative thought patterns and affirming positive ones, you should be able to use this law to your advantage. That's right, you can temporarily influence your life situation by thinking positive. However, this requires substantial effort, and can be exhausting. You are trying to manage your thoughts, which are incredibly impulsive, volatile things. This also reinforces the mind-identified way of being, which as you know is the cause of mental suffering and cuts you off from the peace within.

People want to live an abundant, fulfilled life and there's nothing wrong with that. But striving for those things through the mind state will not lead to that. You may become rich and experience many of the pleasures that this world has to offer, but you will never be truly fulfilled or at peace.

When you dwell in the stillness beyond thought, you are already complete. Nothing else needs to be added to you; there is no identification with thought, therefore there is no sense of needing to be elsewhere or achieve something in order to feel accomplished. Being present is a state of needing nothing. You are fulfilled in the moment. No external thing needs to be added or changed to affirm this. You are connected to something bigger, and this realisation liberates you from the search for fulfilment in the external world. When you are truly in the *here* and *now*, and not identified with the mind, you will be at peace no matter what your current life situation resembles.

So, what does that say about presence, and its state of attraction? Being in the present moment gives you natural access into a fulfilled abundant state. Therefore, because you have a fulfilled abundant energy about you, you will attract abundance into your life in one form or another. It's a paradox; being in a state of needing nothing is the most attractive state there is. This is never the reason for practicing presence, though. You *never* do it in order to bring abundance into your life. That simply happens by default. From this perspective, when things *do* come into your life on the material plane, they are never clung to. They are enjoyed and appreciated, but there is always an understanding that they are temporary and do not define who you are. Looking to the present moment to provide abundance on the material plane ensures you will remain identified with the mind.

Becoming present is about dis-identifying with the mind, which in the process strips away identification with the material world. You are completely letting go of the idea that you will find fulfilment through external things, whether they be money, relationships, or self-improvement. Those things can be enjoyed and appreciated, but once you are conscious, you realise that to look for fulfilment in them is setting yourself up for failure. A life spent chasing the next *thing*, as you will never be complete with what you have right now.

The idea of presence is that you move *beyond* the material plane and into the stillness, which is the source of everything. Where everything on the material plane, including yourself, comes from. In this space, you are already complete and whole. Fulfilled in every sense of the word, irrespective of your life situation.

When you have let go of the material world and have given yourself to the present moment, life responds by manifesting abundance into your life in different ways. That's a fact, and that's the law of attraction in action. When your energy is abundant, then in time what will come into your life will reflect that energy."

Letting Go

Tyson sat down on a stool to the side of the stage, positioned just out of view from the audience. Seemingly out of energy, he needed to rest and give the audience time to digest the substantial content that he was trying to articulate. Head between his legs, he inhaled deeply as he gathered his composure. It would be obvious to any onlooker that the lecture was taking an emotional toll on him. Standing back up after a few minutes, and looking somewhat refreshed, he calmly walked back onto the stage and began to carry on from where he left off.

"Letting go is tough," he stated to audience. "Who

here has had to let go of something when they didn't want to? Hands up." Tyson scanned the room. "Looks like most of us. It's hard I know. Whether it be a relationship, a job, a life situation or any other thing we have the ability to become attached to, letting go hurts. Then there's the ultimate exercise in letting go; death. The death of a loved one has to be the hardest of them all. You are *forced* to let go, regardless of whether you feel ready. Mortality does not consult and respect your mental processes.

I almost became numb to death when I was growing up. In a violent community like Trentan, death becomes normalised. On top of that, I had friends and relatives regularly taken away to prison, sometimes never to be seen again. Letting go of people has been a big part of my life. I had to learn from an early age that, in order to accept and deal with it, I had to accept and deal with the emotions. The pain needs to be embraced. Whether it's caused by a death, loss of a relationship, an ailment in health, or simply a setback in life. They all have the ability to cause emotional pain, just in different degrees. But regardless, the process of dealing with the suffering and moving forward is always the same.

Through my experience, I have learned that no good comes from distracting yourself, or blocking out the pain that comes with such life events. One must embrace the feelings completely, sit with them, and let the emotions run their course. This may take weeks, months, or even years, depending on the level of attachment you had to the person or situation.

But regardless of time, in order to truly move forward and allow room for something positive to emerge, you must be willing to let go. This doesn't mean to *forget*. Letting go when life requires is an act of strength, and allows things to rebalance. Remember that; it's not a selfish act. Again, presence is the answer here. When you bring presence to the process of letting go, it allows to you to sit with the pain and in time dissolve it. All else is madness. You are only prolonging the suffering and making your situation worse.

I know that I can ramble." Tyson stated apologetically to his audience. "In case I have lost or confused any of you along the way, let me try to clarify and explain this topic further, as it applies to all aspects of life."

Tyson took his regular sip of water and breathed deeply before continuing. "Letting go allows the balance of things to remain," he reiterated. "It makes room for new things to emerge into your life. Although people understand this concept, very few really apply it to their life consistently because of the mind-identified state of being. People cling to things, whether it's to a person, a job or a living situation. Whatever it may be, when people hang onto things from a place of neediness or addiction they become unwilling to let go.

Even when things take a turn for the worse, we are known to hang on and be unwilling to let go. This causes a lot of destruction in our lives. Particularly when it comes to relationships. People's unwillingness to let go of a partner, even though the relationship itself is miserable, creates more negativity. The longer you refuse to let go when all the signs are telling you to, the worse it will get.

This addiction is the other side of love. The *dark* side of love, if you will. Often the pain that people feel when they are forced to let go is the addiction being broken; the process of weaning off someone. We sometimes mistake this for heartbreak, when really it is caused by the mind's attachment. Don't get me wrong, letting go of a partner can be one of the most painful experiences you go through, but understanding the truth behind it will allow you to move through it. You must trust and allow the pain to be, and know that it will eventually pass, creating space for something new to manifest.

The process can be very similar to the way an addict responds when weaning themselves away from drug dependency. The pain and anxiety that comes with breaking that addiction is immense, but if he or she can stay present throughout, and not be sucked back into the cycle it will eventually subside.

This addictive process applies to all areas of life, be it relationships, drugs, food, lifestyle and, of course, the thinking itself which is attached to all these things. No matter what, the same principles apply. It's the *mind* that's addicted, not you. If you're identified with your mind, then you will be at the mercy of whatever it relies upon, and you will be dependent upon it for your sense of happiness.

From a state of presence, you will understand how this process works. From this space, you will have the strength to let go of things when the time comes, and not be controlled by the cycle of addiction.

Balance is intrinsically linked to letting go. For your life to remain in balance, you must allow things to come and go without becoming dependent. If you don't, areas of your life will become neglected, and you will experience the pain associated with that."

Balance

"Everything in this world is in balance." Tyson projected to the audience as he walked across the stage. "Your life is balanced out by your actions, be they good or bad. A fundamental law of the universe is that every action has an equal and opposite reaction. Nobody can escape this reality, no matter who you are. Down to the finest details of life, everything is balanced.

Being conscious of this law can give you great faith

in the darkest of times, knowing they will eventually pass and balance out. This is the natural flux of things. However, many of us interfere with this, and prolong the dark times through identification.

Identifying with negative thoughts and feelings about a situation will throw this natural balance off. Instead of letting them come and go, we tend to believe in them, amplifying the situation and blocking light from coming in.

When 'bad times' come, as they inevitably do. Whether it is in regards to health, finance or relationships – the mind is inclined to project a negative story, which is often accompanied by distressing thoughts and feelings. Instinctively, the majority of us will wrestle with this story, engaging with the emotions associated with it, exaggerating it and take action out of this negative space.

One must dis-identify with the negative thoughts and feelings. Sit with the emotions, feel them in their entirety, and embrace the pain; it *will* eventually pass. While doing this, always stay conscious. Feel the energy associated with the emotions, but don't get lost in your thoughts. If you do this, and really stay present, the darkness will begin to lift, allowing you to connect with the peace underneath.

From this space, you will now understand the situation for what it is and have clarity moving forward. You are now dealing with the circumstances from a place of consciousness, a place that is not identified with the story in your head. Bringing presence to the situation will allow the universal law of balance to play out. You will begin to manifest whatever is needed to balance out the situation at hand; that's the law in action. Life balances out in perfect harmony if you do not interfere with its natural flux."

Taking a break from his discourse material, Tyson went back to telling the story of his friendship with Joey. The audience welcomed the change in pace and focused in as Tyson continued from where he had left off.

"So to set the scene again, we were sitting in a diner in Trentan. Joey had come down for a tour of the neighbourhood." He said with a chuckle. "But seriously, you got to respect the young man. He was a million miles from the safety of the suburbs at this point. Anyway, here we go...bear with me while I recollect."

After lunch, Tyson proposed that they take a walk around his neighbourhood. He wanted to show Joey what his reality looked like. Although Joey was nervous, he obliged, as he knew it would be important to the teachings. They got up from the table and walked out into the main street of Trentan. It was a hive of activity, with people going about their daily business.

Tyson looked out over the street as he spoke. "See this place, it has two realities. Right now, there are families everywhere. People working, shopping and kids playing in the street. After dark, that all changes. The feigns come out for their fix. The prostitutes line the streets, and we run the corners. It's a melting pot, brother. There's danger around every corner. To survive out here at night, you have to be present. If you're off in your head, distracted by thought, you are going to slip up, and the consequences for doing so are unforgiving. That's why I am the way I am. These streets raised me, and I had to learn how to survive on them. These truths that I'm passing onto you were developed out here through adversity. Under the chaos, I found peace. I don't mind telling you, that's very rare out here.

But it's my time now. The streets have served their purpose, and shown me the truth. I must move on now, and apply what I've learnt into a new environment. I'm destined to transcend this place Joey, and somehow you are connected to that. I just know it."

Joey was surprised by Tyson's words. "But how am I connected? How can I possibly help you? Don't get me wrong; I'd love to. I just don't know how."

Tyson didn't have the answer either, but he had faith it would clarify. "In time, my friend, it will all reveal itself. It might not be you directly; it might come through you and lead me to something else that provides me with the opportunity. For now, it's all a mystery, but I have to embrace that – trust in the unknown and continue to give myself to the *now*. That's the only way. Everything else is madness. This can't be figured out with the analytical mind.

Anyway – I want to show you something. Let's take a walk down the block."

Tyson led Joey down the main street, shepherding him to a dingy side street around the corner. Joey grew apprehensive as they approached a crew of young guys hanging outside the entrance to a building, but Tyson proceeded to walk up to them and shake their hands.

"Sup, boys. How's the training going? You're looking in shape, Jay," Tyson said to one of the guys.

"Who's your friend, Ty? Never seen him around here," one of the guys said sarcastically.

"This is Joey. I'm showing him around town. Don't worry – I vouch for him. There's a purpose to all this," Tyson responded assertively. With that, they made their way into a local boxing gym. The guys outside were left confused by Joey's presence, but they knew better to question Tyson. He had a lot of respect in the neighbourhood, especially amongst the younger generation.

The boxing gym was busy with guys skipping and working the bags. A trainer stood in the ring, holding up pads for a younger fighter. Tyson ushered Joey around, showing him the varied equipment and pointing out some of the great fighters that covered the walls.

"This is a very important aspect of my life, Joey. I've boxed for years. The training is like none other; it keeps you both physically and mentally fit. It requires serious discipline and focus if you want to compete in the ring. In many ways it's like life; if you're disciplined and focused, you will be successful. If you are inconsistent and distracted, you will fail to step up to the challenge when the time requires. You have to be conditioned for it."

Tyson continued to explain the various parallels between boxing and life. It was obvious to Joey that he was incredibly passionate about the sport. He was a little confused as to how it applied to the teachings though.

"So does that mean I need to take up boxing as well? The training looks pretty gruelling," Joey asked.

"No! Not at all. That wasn't the reason for bringing you here. It was to show you that to live a life of presence, it helps if you establish a disciplined routine. Discipline and routine can help to keep you in the present moment. I use boxing, as it keeps me physically fit, but also helps to build upon the foundation of presence in my life. It requires substantial focus every time I enter the gym, bringing me deeper into the *now*. While training I'm completely immersed in the doing, thought has no room to come in. It's like a physical form of meditation. It doesn't have to be boxing – it could be anything. Something that requires your full awareness and that you can consistently apply to your life."

It made sense to Joey. He could see the benefits of Tyson's routine, and was looking forward to creating his own. After the gym Tyson escorted Joey back to his car, making sure he got there safely.

"Thanks for today, man. It was amazing coming to your neighbourhood," Joey said.

Tyson was happy to show off the positive aspects of Trentan for a change. "It's all good, brother. You just focus on applying presence into your life. I'll call to arrange another meet in a week or so. Take care."

Tyson strolled back to his apartment block and Joey drove home to the suburbs, feeling completely inspired. With every teaching, Joey could feel himself becoming more alive and connected to his reality. The fog of anxiety and depression that clouded his life for so long was now a light mist. Clearing further with every passing day.

9

Being

The week that followed was one of deep peace for Joey. He never knew that such tranquillity existed in the world. He dwelled in this state without any worry for the future. He spent days simply *being*, walking around his neighbourhood and appreciating the reality that he once despised. He noticed his interactions with people completely changed. His peaceful state clearly resonated with them.

He was now in a state of *being*, no longer identified with the mind. As he resided in the stillness, he observed that when he was required to practically use his mind, his thinking was clear and powerful. Answers and ideas would intuitively come to him. From this perspective, his mind was his friend, and benefited the practical aspects of his life; everything from his study to everyday problem solving. He was somewhat perplexed by this, as he knew that dis-identifying with the mind was the key to his state of presence, but at the same time he understood that the mind was needed for practical reasons. He just didn't know how the two could co-exist. This was something he wanted to clarify with Tyson.

A week after their last meeting, Tyson called Joey to see how he was going and organise another catch-up as he had promised. He suggested that he come to Joey this time. Joey agreed and offered to show Tyson around his neighbourhood, as he had done for him. Tyson liked the idea, and they arranged to meet at a local cafe strip on the Saturday coming.

Joey was excited to see him and share his progress. He had come a long way in the last week as he continued to detach from his mind and enter a stronger state of presence. He was also beginning to see how life began to flow with ease as a result.

Saturday came and Joey was up early, fitting in some study before he met Tyson for lunch. He had a renewed focus and energy for university. In the past, he would procrastinate and leave his assignments to the last minute. Now he was proactive, chipping away at his studies consistently each day. Creating the disciplined routine that was needed for him to be successful.

On the other side of town, Tyson was still resting in bed. As usual he had been out to the early hours of the morning, organising his crew and dealing with the many issues that came with running a drug operation. He was exhausted, and was trying to catch up on as much sleep as possible before the meeting.

Midday came and Joey arrived at the café strip, which consisted of a few food options and a couple of high-end fashion outlets. Joey waited on the sidewalk, keeping a look out for Tyson. He eventually arrived in a cab.

"Tyson! Over here," Joey called out.

Tyson signalled to him and walked over.

"What's up, bro! The main street looks a bit different than Trentan," Tyson said with a chuckle. "I'm starving, what's for lunch?"

"I'm thinking burgers," Joey replied. "The joint on the corner does a pretty good one."

"Lead the way, sounds like my kind of meal," Tyson responded.

They arrived at the burger bar and found themselves a seat overlooking the main street. They were both hungry, so wasted no time in ordering.

"So, how's things?" Tyson asked.

"Couldn't be better," said Joey. "I've undergone significant changes since I last saw you. I feel like I've rooted myself further into the present moment, and have been experiencing a deep sense of joy and peace because of it. On the external, nothing has changed about my life situation, except that I now view it from a place of

TYSON & JOEY

acceptance rather than denial. I feel like life is beginning to flow. The struggle and frustration is no longer there, and as a result, I'm much more productive in everything I do. The anxiety and depression isn't weighing me down, I feel like I've risen above those dark clouds, and can now see them for what they are – an illusion created by the mind. Empowered only if I engage."

"I'm glad," Tyson replied. "I'm glad you've seen the truth, and can now experience the peace and joy that I have been talking about. I can see it in you; your energy is calm, and you no longer seem anxious. That's not to say the mind won't try to test you and claw you back in. It will. As long as you are grounded in the moment, though, it will never have the power to engage you like it did in the past. Keep practising presence, and your light will continue to grow brighter."

"I wanted to ask you about the mind, and how it can be used from a state of presence," Joey asked. "I realise that being identified with the mind is the cause of mental suffering, but I also realise that the mind is essential for the practical aspects of everyday life. So how is it possible to detach but also use it? Doesn't that contradict your teachings?"

"Great question," Tyson said. "Yes, the truth that I have been preaching is about bringing yourself out of thought, which is the mind, and into the present moment.

114

That is the truth, and is the only place you will find the peace that you have been experiencing. However, like you said, your mind is still needed for practical everyday things, like problem solving, making plans, studying and so on. The mind is positive and helpful from this perspective.

I call this practical thinking, and when applied from a state of presence, it is incredibly powerful. The thinking I am talking about dis-identifying with is the constant stream of thought that narrates, compares and judges every aspect of your life. It's the thinking that you can't stop, which becomes the cause of immense psychological suffering when you identify with it. The mind is a tool, Joey. It's there to be used for practical reasons only. Outside of that it's incredibly destructive."

Your Mind is a Tool

"You'll be relieved to know that I don't have much time left," Tyson told his audience. The comment was intended as a light-hearted joke, but the attendees seemed genuinely disappointed. "You'll excuse me, then, if I make another segue.

You see, the mind is a powerful tool. When applied practically it can do amazing things, as I'm sure you have experienced or witnessed. It solves problems, generates ideas, identifies patterns, makes connections and continues the advancement of technology.

However, this is a double-edged sword. The mind is also very destructive. Identification with the mind is the reason why countless people suffer from mental illness and addiction. For the majority of people, it has taken over their lives. The mind controls them, instead of them controlling *it*. Once this happens, they can no longer distinguish between their mind and their true nature.

When you are identified with the mind, you are at the mercy of its reactive, volatile nature. Consequently, when the thoughts turn negative and the self-talk becomes dark, you begin to experience the negative feelings that are associated.

From a conscious, present state you are dis-identified with your mind and thoughts. From this space, you are able to watch the thoughts come and go without engaging with them – the negative self-talk has no power. It simply comes and goes without attachment.

Now, you *can* use your mind productively, applying it like a tool to a problem you want to solve or an opportunity you want to research. From this perspective, your mind is your friend, and will enable you to achieve great things in whatever area you choose.

Like a tool, once you've finished applying it to a task you put it away until it's needed again. This way of living enables you to operate successfully in the world. It allows you to use the mind in its full capacity, and then detach from it, creating space for you to retreat back into the stillness beyond thought.

'Thinking' from this perspective is productive, used when necessary. When you apply thinking from presence it is incredibly clear and energised. You will notice how quickly answers arise, and how effortlessly you begin to make connections between subject matter and generate solutions to the problem at hand.

So there are two types of thinking at play. 'Practical thinking', which can be consciously applied to a situation at will, and 'impractical thinking', the constant stream of thought that analyses every aspect of your life. Volatile and often negative in nature. Becoming clear about the dynamics of thought and how it affects you is the first step. From there, you can differentiate between the types and begin to apply thinking in the way it's meant to be used. Do not be a slave to your mind. It's a powerful tool, and therefore can be powerful in a positive or negative way. Remember, it works for you, not the other way around.

There will be many things that will cause you confusion in these early stages of becoming present. A word of advice – don't feel the need to know all the answers immediately. They will clarify in time, and you should learn to embrace the 'not knowing'. That's showing true faith and trust in life. The mind will resist this. It has to know *everything*; therefore, it will try to drag you back into thought to figure the unknown out. Stay present in these times and bring yourself further into the *now*. Not knowing the answers, and what my future held, is what led me to be here tonight." Tyson added, returning to the tale of his lunch with Joey.

"So what's new in your world?" Joey had asked.

"Same old, my friend. Still hustling the streets until my opportunity to transcend presents itself."

"So what do you want to do instead of the streets?"

"That's not entirely clear at the moment. All I know is that I need to go legit, and apply my knowledge into another area. I'm talking about the message that I'm passing onto you. I'm starting to believe that my purpose is to bring it to the world. I just need the right outlet."

"You should write a book!" Joey suggested. "Your message is powerful, and could help a lot of people."

Tyson sat back and let the idea sink in. "Interesting. I never thought of a book. To be honest, I don't know how I will bring these truths to the world, but I feel like I'm destined to."

"I know a lady!" Joey said excitedly. "A family friend is involved in publishing. Maybe I can get you a meeting with her?"

Tyson was taken aback by the suggestion. Nobody had ever offered to help him like that. A book. Hmm....maybe that's the opportunity I've been waiting on. I don't know, I did always say you would be somehow connected to it...remember? I said that to you after our first meeting. This could be it, brother."

"It would be my pleasure to connect you with her," Joey replied, elated to finally have something to offer Tyson. "You have shown me the truth about my suffering, and I am now in a great space. I can't thank you enough for that. I also believe your message needs to be told. Your story needs to be told Tyson. You forged this understanding through adversity. It's truly inspiring."

"Thank you Joey, that means a lot to me. But you know, my writing skills are not at that level. If I'm going to articulate this story, I'll need a lot of guidance in that area. I'm a talker, not a writer. Plus, this is going to take time, time I don't really have. I'm stuck in a cycle. I have to keep dealing to support my family. There's no other option."

"I'll help you," Joey said. "I've developed writing skills through my education. I can provide you with any support you need."

"What about time?" Tyson asked. "When are we supposed to get this done? Like I said, I've got limited availability. It's not as though I can take paid leave from the streets to write a manuscript. I don't think that will go down well with the crew."

"You want to get off the streets, don't you?" Joey snapped, a little sharper than he'd intended. "Well, you are going to have to transition someone else into your position. Maybe taking some time away to write your story will allow this to happen. This is your opportunity, Tyson, and you know it. In two weeks, I'll have the whole summer off from university. That's almost three months. We can write it over that time. And don't worry about finances; I have plenty to go around, for you and your family. That's how much I believe in this idea."

Tyson was shocked by Joey's compassion. "You would do that for me?"

"Of course, that's nothing compared to what you've given me. Like I said before, money is not an issue. Benefits of being born into a privileged family, remember? If it makes it easier for you to accept, you can pay me back once you're a bestseller. How about that?"

Tyson couldn't speak. Tears ran down his checks. He was completely overwhelmed with emotion. The opportunity that he had been patiently waiting for had finally arrived. He got up from his seat and hugged Joey.

"Thank you, brother."

"OK, let me stop the story right there." Tyson said as he paused his narrative. "So, this was it. The opportunity I had been waiting on just fell into my lap – seemingly out of nowhere. Funny how life works isn't it?

But know this; I always had faith that it would come, and allow me to transcend my environment. I just didn't know how or when. But I trusted, even in the darkest of times. That's the difference.

This applies to all of you out there!" Tyson declared sternly to the audience. "All of you have goals or desires that you want to achieve in life, otherwise you wouldn't be here. Am I right? Mine was to transcend the street life and provide for my family, yours maybe be related to any number of things. Whatever it is, they share the common ground that they are a future ideal. That word – *future* – is the down fall, and the reason many of these goals will never be met.

You need to let go of the future to get there," Tyson reiterated. "As you know from my story, the opportunity which brought me here today did not come through chasing a future ideal. It came through recognising that I wanted to transcend my reality and giving myself fully to the present moment – *trusting* that it would happen when the time was right. Absolute faith is what I had, and through that the life I wanted began to manifest".

Tyson let his words sink in with the audience before continuing his story.

After lunch Joey showed Tyson around his neighbourhood, including his university. Tyson never been to a campus before, and was keen to see the different facilities. Joey showed him the library and the computer labs.

"This is where we can start drafting your book. I have twenty-four hour access to these services, so we can work around your schedule," Joey announced.

After the campus tour, they went back to Joey's place. His father was home, and was very intrigued to learn that Tyson was from Trentan. He had a thousand questions about his neighbourhood, and what he did for a living. Before he got into too much detail, Joey interjected and took Tyson around the rest of the house. The back yard had a pool and entertainment area, so they decided to relax out there and enjoy the sun.

"It's been a great day. Thanks for showing me around your neighbourhood," Tyson said. "It sure is different over this side of the bridge. I feel a million miles from Trentan."

"Anytime. I'm really looking forward to working with you on this project. It reinforces a truth that is missing in today's society. I truly believe you can help a lot of people," Joey replied.

"It feels right, Joey. The stars are aligning, brother. I'm destined to do this. We are all here to do something;

we all have a purpose while we are here on earth, but the majority of us never figure it out or are too scared to follow it. I know this is my purpose. It's so clear to me now."

"You truly believe we're all here to do something special?" Joey asked.

"Most definitely," Tyson said. "We all have something that we are meant to do; something unique to us."

Life Purpose

"There is something you are destined to do while you're here," Tyson announced to his audience. "Something specific and unique to you. Look around, it's obvious. The people who are most content are those pursuing things that are true to them.

We are all so distracted by our life situation that we never become still long enough to figure out our truth. Even for people who find that purpose, many don't pursue it through fear or laziness. Then there are those that try and convince themselves they have. As a result, they fall short in their goals as the passion and purpose is not connected.

Never force a vision for yourself out of thought, as it won't be true for you. It must come organically, from consciousness. Once it rises within it will be unmistakable, and you will know without a shadow of doubt that it's what you are intended to do.

As long as you are striving for things that are not true, you will never be fulfilled. It's like going against the current; there will always be a feeling of discontent. Those that accept this, and begin to become still in the world, will find this truth. From there, it's a matter of overcoming fear through faith and having the courage and drive to pursue it.

Everybody is unique, and has something that they can bring to the world. Some people's truth will take them to pursue music, some sports, and others the sciences. Whatever it is, there is a void that is waiting for you to fill. There is a spot for *you* that nobody else can fill. Find your truth, fill this void, and life will open up to you. Don't be like the majority of people, who ignore it. That only leads to discontentment, no matter how successful you become.

As soon as you start pursuing what is right for you, the inner struggle will subside. You will feel a sense of freedom and ease when approaching your work. From this space, you can't help but be successful. You are now flowing with the current. You can lean back into life and let the magic unfold."

"So there's something that I'm meant do while I'm

here as well?" Joey asked.

"Of course," Tyson replied. "There's a divine plan and purpose for all of us, unique to every person. You already know it on a deeper level, you just have to stay present long enough for it to surface. You can't figure it out with the analytical mind; it must arise out of presence. Always remember, your life situation is secondary to your greater purpose, which is to be a vehicle for consciousness. To be completely rooted in the *now*, no matter what. Only then will the life that is true for you begin to manifest.

From the mind-identified state of being, often things that you think are right for you end up being incompatible. You see that everywhere, especially in people's relationships. From a state of presence, what is true for you will arise from within and resonate. There will be a knowing that it is true for you, and no matter what you do, nothing will change that. Letting go is fundamental to this. Always be willing to let go of something. If it continues to ring true and come back, then you will know it's meant to be."

This was a topic that Tyson continued to explain to Joey as they relaxed by the pool. Joey was thirsty for knowledge and had countless questions, which Tyson was more than happy to answer. However, he knew Joey needed to be patient and let things come to him on life's terms. From his perspective, he was simply planting the seeds that would grow with life experience. As night began to fall, Tyson felt the streets calling him home. It was time for him to head back to Trentan, and to prepare for the night ahead.

"It's about that time, Joey. I better head back," Tyson said as the sun began to fade. "Thanks for today. I'm excited to work with you on the project, it feels right. I'll begin drafting ideas in my spare time, and we can get started in a few weeks once I have my affairs in place."

"Sounds good," Joey responded. "My studies will be wrapped up soon, so that works out perfectly. In the meantime, I'll continue to practice presence. Let me know if you need anything, and remember I'm all in on this project. I've got the resources, facilities and connections to make this work. It's your time! You helped me, and now I'm returning the favour."

"You're a good man, Joey. I better go. I'll see you in a few."

Tyson jumped in a cab and headed off into the night. Leaving the suburbs behind for the concrete jungle that he called home. He always knew he needed to leave the street life, but suddenly felt urgency unlike any he had experienced before. He knew it was only a matter of time before the lifestyle caught up with him.

10

Transcending

Tyson was immersed in the streets. He lived and breathed the lifestyle. He knew that leaving it behind would come with resistance; not only from his peers, but also from himself. Change brought its own fear and sadness, and he would be leaving behind all that he knew, including his home. Nevertheless, he had to do it. Not only for him and his family, but for the community at large. To make real change in the neighbourhood, he needed to be able to give back, both financially and as a role model. He wanted to show that there are other avenues outside of crime, especially to the younger generation.

Over the following week, Tyson began making strategic changes in his operation that would allow him time to work on his manuscript. His goal was to move away altogether, but in the short term, he needed to get his crew used to Jimmy running the show. This would be essential to Tyson's transition. If he left his operation with no structure in place, he knew things would fall apart, resulting in violence and bloodshed in the streets. He cared for his crew greatly, and in many ways, he felt responsible for their ongoing well being.

Although Tyson needed the stars to align, with everything from the streets to the writing of his book, he had no doubts about the direction he was moving in. He had great faith and trust that it was all destined. The opportunity had come out of stillness, and therefore he knew it was true for him. He simply had to keep giving himself to the *now* and trust in his instincts. This had allowed him to survive and succeed on the streets so far, and had brought Joey and this opportunity into his life.

It was the early hours of Saturday morning, and Tyson had been taking a back-seat approach to the night's operations, giving Jimmy the reigns and offering him guidance where needed. Tyson had been on edge for the past hour. He felt something wasn't right, but he put it down to nerves because of the changes he was implementing. He couldn't shake the sensation, though. He knew something was up, but he continued to ignore it. With just one hour left in the shift before daybreak, he decided to push on.

The customer base was split between local feigns and visitors. Most of the regulars were known by face and name; they were usually heavily addicted, and lived on the streets. They purchased small bags, just enough to get a fix for a few hours before coming back for more. The real money was with the out-of-towners. They would drive in from the northern suburbs and buy in greater quantities for their parties and gatherings.

The actual dealing of the drugs had a system to it, which for the most part worked seamlessly. Upon arriving at the corner spot, whether by car or on foot, the customer would put in an order with one of the crew. This would be communicated back to a runner who would collect the drugs from the stash, which was hidden out of sight from the street. The cash would be passed over to the dealer in the meantime, and the runner would deliver the goods to complete the transaction. This happened continually throughout the night and depending on how busy it was would determine the number of dealers and runners at any one time.

Tyson played a managerial role, watching the operations from a distance and intervening where he needed to. He had a keen eye for picking out undercover cops, and would signal to the crew when he spotted them. It wasn't just the cops that he had to worry about, though; it was also rival crews. There was constant tension over territory, with operations trying to expand into one another's turf. He tried to mitigate any issues where possible, but inevitably, expansion was met with resistance and violence.

Tyson could read the streets, and for so long this had enabled him to survive and thrive out there. This night was different, however. He had ignored his intuition.

As he watched a blacked-out SUV pull up to the kerb, he knew something wasn't right. As the transaction proceeded, he watched on nervously from a distance. The dealer went up, took the order and communicated it back to the runner. The runner went and collected the drugs, which were stashed down a side alley. While this was happening, the cash was supposed to be passed to the dealer, but the customer held things up by arguing over the price. The runner came back with the goods and passed them to the dealer. As he did, the back window lowered and a pistol came out. Two shots were fired, dropping both crewmembers. The driver's door opened and the drugs were collected, before the SUV sped off into the night. Jimmy who was across the street at the time, pulled out his gun and shot into the back of the vehicle as it sped off.

Tyson ran over and began helping Dion and Jay, who had been shot in the incident. Dion, who was only 15, had been shot to the head and killed instantly; Jay had taken a bullet to the shoulder, and was losing blood quickly. Tyson was in shock as he held Dion, staring at his lifeless body. He was instantly consumed by anger towards the people who had committed this despicable act, and full of guilt over his role in allowing it to happen. He had known that something was up, but ignored his instincts. Now a young man had paid the price for his lack of focus.

"Get Jay to hospital!" he yelled.

Jimmy jumped into his car parked across the street and pulled up to the corner where the guys were laying. Tyson loaded Jay into the back seat and told Jimmy to drive as fast as he could to Saint John's Hospital, which was ten minutes away. Jimmy sped off and Tyson dropped back to his knees, cradling Dion in his arms as he broke down in tears.

Tyson woke after a restless night. This latest casualty had rocked him to the core. Death wasn't new, but seeing someone so young killed senselessly in front of his eyes was too much for him to handle. Not only that, but he felt responsible for the death. He was the one that was supposed to look out for his crew, and he was the one who had gone against his own judgement and decided to carry on dealing.

He was done with the street life. He didn't have the stomach for it anymore. Last night confirmed this; it was another sign that he had to get out before he became the next casualty. He felt death was calling him. He knew he couldn't delay his actions any longer; that the time was now. He had to take the first step, and begin working on his project.

The death of Dion caused Tyson to realise that his presence in the streets was no longer beneficial for his crew, even as a guide to Jimmy. He had planned on slowly moving away from it, gently nudging Jimmy into position, but he knew he could only concentrate on one thing. Juggling both would only affect his judgement, as it did that fateful night.

Tyson felt a sense of relief with his decision to leave the streets immediately. He informed Jimmy, who to his surprise was completely supportive of the change. He was confident that he could successfully take over Tyson's command.

"You've been my right-hand man for years now Jimmy, I've got to leave though. I have to do what's true for me, brother. Dealing doesn't make sense anymore. I'm destined for other things, man. I'm not leaving for good, though; I just need to remove myself from the environment until I am in a position to give back. I hope you understand."

"You've always been destined for greater things Tyson, we all see that. You're wasting your potential out here. Don't worry about me, I've learnt a lot from you. I know I can survive and succeed on these streets, just like you have," Jimmy responded.

"Thank you, Jimmy. I wasn't sure how you would react. I thought there would be resistance to me leaving, but you've proved me wrong on that one. I'm glad you've taken note of how I operate out there, but also learn from the other night. That happened because of me. I knew something didn't feel right, I just knew it, but I ignored my instincts and didn't call it off. Never compromise your instincts, Jimmy; always follow that guidance. That's the key to surviving out there. And when you're ready, something that's true for you will come along as well. Always be open to that. Drug dealing is unsustainable. You need an exit strategy into something legitimate."

In that moment, Tyson gave it all up. He let go of the streets, and took his first step into the unknown. Although it terrified him, he had complete trust in his new direction.

Failing to Win

Taking a break from his narrative once more, Tyson made his way to the front of the stage and sat casually on its edge. Peering through the bright lights, he focused in on the audience and began to go deeper. Discussing the point behind his aforementioned story.

"Don't think I got here today without failing and making countless mistakes along the way," he grimly explained. "I don't want you to come under the illusion that this intuition I talk about was clear cut, kindly transitioning me into where I needed to go. Not at all! These signs that I followed led me into countless mistakes and failures. Many times, I was led into harm's way, or lost out financially. However, every single time, without exception, I was taught a valuable lesson.

Failure may look negative on the surface, setting you back in one way or another, but there is always a lesson in it. If realised, that lesson will change the course you are heading down for the better. However, the majority will never see it like that. Failure will always be viewed as a setback, an attack on one's life situation in one way or another. From this perspective, there is never a lesson learned.

Like I said, I'm not an exception. My past is full of hindrances, and it took me time to find the lesson in them. Years, in fact, I was stuck in a life of crime, repeating the same mistakes, and I justified it to myself, believing I didn't have a choice in my actions. In the end I knew, that if I was to transcend, I needed to look at the results of my actions head-on. Accept, and learn from them. If I had not accepted, then I would still be on the streets today. Actually, I'd most likely be dead or in prison," Tyson said in a matter of fact way.

"The people who become successful out there have almost *always* failed along the way. The only difference between them, and those who do not achieve their goals, is the perspective they take. Those that succeed see failure as a lesson. Those who do not, take it personally.

How do you train yourself to view failure as a lesson? More importantly how do you find the lesson in what is likely to be a high stress situation? Well the anwer is simple – *presence*. The old faithful that is at the core of all acceptance. Staying present amongst the chaos of failure will allow the lesson to rise to the surface.

This makes complete sense, doesn't it?" Tyson asked the audience rhetorically. "What's the alternative? You indulge in the relentless stream of thought that's running through your mind, exaggerate the situation and take action out of that space? Will that help? That's sure to make things worse, but that's what most us do – completely missing the lesson in the process. The sad thing is, people repeat these cycles over and over again. You see it everywhere, particularly in relationships. One failed relationship after another, people stay on the hamster wheel, coming up against the same issues and never knowing why.

You have to find the lesson in your failures," Tyson reiterated to the audience. "Otherwise, that will be you. Stuck on the loop in one form or another, repeating the same bullshit, which is absolute insanity. And if I'm not mistaken, isn't that the actual definition of the word? I believe Einstein said, "insanity is doing the same thing over and over again and expecting different results." So,

I guess by Einstein's definition most of you out there are insane," Tyson said with a chuckle. "But seriously this is what a lot of us a dealing with, stuck in cycles perpetuated by our minds.

Presence is the answer, you need to detach from the mind and bring yourself out of thought. This will break through these negative cycles and set you on the right track to reach your goals."

11

New Day

Joey had finished his end of year exams, and was thoroughly ready for a holiday. He hadn't heard from Tyson in weeks, and was wondering whether he was still keen on the book idea they had discussed. Joey was now in a good space; he had been continuing to practice presence, and applying it to all aspects of his life. This enabled him to bring a high level of focus to his study, and avoid the stress that came along with it. More importantly, the anxiety and depression was now a distant cloud that posed no threat; he felt as though he was out of the storm, and had the tools in place if it ever came back.

He was enjoying his first day of holidays when he got a call from Tyson.

"Joey! How are you, bro? Long time no talk," Tyson said.

"Tyson, it's been a while. I'm great! Just finished up at university for the year. I'm on holiday now, so I have a lot of free time. Are you still keen on developing your manuscript?" Joey asked.

"I'm ready, brother. The past week has shown me that the street life is no longer an option for me. The death of a young friend made me realise that I have to act now. So I gave it all up. I'm ready to give myself fully to the opportunity that we discussed. It feels right. I know we can develop something meaningful."

"I'm sorry to hear about the death of your friend," Joey responded. "I can't imagine the pain you're in right now. Like I said before though, I believe in this project. You've turned my life around, and you can do the same for others. I've got the time and resources to make this happen, so when you're ready just let me know."

"It's a relief to hear you say that," Tyson replied. "I'm glad you still want to help. I want to get started right away; I really need to get the ball rolling with this project. Without the streets, I'm in a precarious position. I have a bit of rainy day cash stashed away, but financially, I need for this to work."

"It's going to work," Joey reinforced. "Like you said, you're destined to bring your story to the world. You're taking the first step in the right direction, and I'm here to support you in any way I can. That's the least I can do. You've given me so much – before I met you I was at a loss. I was a complete stranger. You saw what I needed, and showed me how to connect with that inner peace."

"My pleasure," Tyson replied. "Cool! So, how about we meet up tomorrow and discuss how we're going to approach this thing?"

"Sounds good. Where would you like to meet?"

Tyson considered the options for a moment. "I wouldn't mind getting out of Trentan after what's happened. How about we meet in the central city this time? I haven't been there forever. We could do the usual and grab some lunch?"

"Sounds like a plan!" Joey confirmed.

They were both feeling good about the collaboration. Joey believed in Tyson and his message, and was confident he had the resources to help him succeed. For Tyson, he realised this was the opportunity he had been waiting for, and he was willing to give it his everything. There was no plan B. This *had* to work.

The following day, they met at a lunch bar in the heart of the city. The place was buzzing with office workers streaming between high-rise buildings, dodging tourists and squeezing between gridlocked traffic. Tyson enjoyed the change in atmosphere.

"The energy out here is like nothing else. You can feel the shift as soon as you arrive in the city. It's chaotic, but

I enjoy the hustle and bustle. People from all walks of life coming together to do business, just as we are," he claimed, sitting back and observing the busy streets.

"It's interesting to people watch. You can really see the unconscious conditioning. People going through the motions, away in their head, completely disconnected from the *now*."

He looked at Joey before continuing. "This is the unconscious state of being that pervades our society. It keeps us going to the jobs we hate, and living lives that aren't true for us. Out of fear we stay on the hamster wheel, hanging onto the prospect of salvation in the future. That, one day, we will reach the level of success that society demands and be fulfilled. It's all an illusion, brother. As long as you are identified with your mind, no matter what you achieve you will never be content. It's an endless tunnel. Even when you do acquire what the mind thinks it needs, it will only keep you satisfied temporarily, until it creates another future ideal that must be met."

Tyson went quiet for a minute as he sipped his water and looked out over the crowds. "If only people knew that the present moment was all they ever needed to focus on. If only they knew that when it becomes the primary focus the other things come with ease. The material things are the icing on the cake, nothing more."

Joey let Tyson's words sink in before responding. "I see the conditioning in myself, and I see it in other people. It's bizarre when I think back to before I met you. I was simply going through the motions as well, never really engaging with my reality. It's scary to think what would have happened to me if I hadn't been shown the truth. I was spiralling out of control....man! I take none of this for granted."

Tyson had seen the bigger picture from day one. He knew they had something important to offer each other. "We came together at the right time. I showed you peace, and now you've provided me with an opportunity. The universe works in mysterious ways, my friend. You have to flow with life, and trust that what is destined for you is unfolding. To trust means to let go and give yourself to the present moment, and follow your intuition. This will always take you to where you need to be. If you live like this, no matter what situation comes into your life, you will always be able to respond to it with whatever the situation requires. The right action will be there when you need it."

They began to discuss the project in more detail. Tyson explained the time and processes involved in publishing a book of this nature, which he had found through his research. Joey was surprised about the amount of work involved and became a little nervous as the reality dawned on him.

Tyson was direct, so there would be no confusion going into the project. "This is it, Joey. This project will take over our lives. I'm giving it to you straight so you have a chance to back out if you feel like you can't commit. We have the idea, now we have to put in the work. That's going to take time and resources, and a whole lot of discipline to get the book to the point where it needs to be."

Joey was nervous, but offered Tyson his full support. "You know I'm in. I believe in this project one hundred percent. I'm just getting my head around the amount of work that needs to be done."

"My man! There's a lot involved obviously, so I completely understand you being nervous, but it doesn't have to be painful. By applying presence to the project, it will flow and manifest as it's supposed to. But if we get caught up in the mind and get stressed and end up taking action out of that space, the project will surely fail. All creativity comes out of the *now* Joey, not out of the mind. To create something that connects with people, the story must be written from consciousness.

But, before we can start work of any kind, we need a crystal-clear vision about the project and what we intend to produce. This is a vital part of the creation process and applies to all facets of life."

Creating

Breaking from the narrative and engaging with his lecture material, Tyson began to explain the fundamentals behind the creation process. "There is a pattern to everything, and there is absolutely one for creating. This event tonight is proof – I wouldn't be here without the book that made my name. The conscious creation process involves visualising, having faith, letting go and receiving," Tyson told his assembled followers in the auditorium.

"To visualise means to become clear about what it is you are intending to create, whether it be related to your career, business, relationship or health. Having a clear vision is essential. Then you must step into that vision, and feel it with all your senses.

Most importantly, the vision must be true for *you*. It must come from a state of presence, organically rising within – it will then be in line with your life purpose. Trying to force a vision that is not true for you is futile. You will never be able to hold it, and will find it difficult to feel in its fullness, which is absolutely necessary.

As mentioned, having faith and letting go are connected to the creation process. To have faith is to let go and trust that your vision is going to manifest. To trust is to stay present, and not worry about the when, where or how it's going to manifest. When you are present, you have completely let go of the vision, giving yourself to the *now*, knowing that what you have asked for is on its way. This is showing absolute faith.

Receiving is allowing space for your vision to manifest. This point can be very overwhelming as something new is emerging into your life, and therefore the intensity of the situation can cause you to retreat, as you are not prepared for change. Again, at this point one must stay present and allow the manifestation to come into reality. Embrace the intensity, knowing that it is the final step in the process.

Another way of looking at this final step is that it's always darkest before the dawn. After letting go, and prior to your manifestation coming into your reality, there will be a dark period of doubt. For a lot of people, this period of doubt kills the creation process before the manifestation arrives.

One must have firm faith during this dark period, and know that it is just part of the process. The intensity of these doubtful thoughts and feelings will keep increasing, until the energy builds up to a point where you may think you cannot take it anymore. At this point, stay present. Your manifestation is close.

Also, know that what you've visualised will never come in the exact form that you envisaged. It will manifest in the divine form that is true for you. It will arrive in a way that is unexpected, and the timing will always be perfect. Things come into your life when they are supposed to, not when you want them to. That's why patience is so essential.

Another important note is that before a manifestation arrives, there will be signs that it's coming; glimpses of your impending attraction. This might come in the form of an experience that gives you a feeling of what you want, or a person or situation that seems to be the perfect fit. These signs are only fleeting; they are not the actual manifestation. Only glimpses into what is coming.

This is where people often lose faith. They take the signs as the actual manifestation. Therefore, once they go away and prove not to be true, they are left disheartened and lose faith in the process altogether. Once you are aware of the process, these signs will simply serve as confirmation that your vision is coming.

The law of attraction is a popular topic, and is definitely not the basis of what I'm advocating here. There are many self-help books that focus on that topic alone. They describe how to manifest your desires by thinking about something and believing and visualising that it is going to happen. There are truths in that, but they miss such a fundamental part – *presence*. Such teachings overlook this foundation and rely on the power of thought alone.

Thoughts can make you very sick. They are volatile, up and down, and can cause anxiety and depression. Getting past – or above – thought is the key. Once you are in this space, you can observe and detach from your thoughts. This is where your true power lies. From this foundation, you consciously decide what you want and it comes from a place of truth. From here, a path becomes clear. Random events will coincide and guide you to where you need to be. All you have to do is flow in the direction that life is steering you.

There is a process involved when bringing something into manifestation. From a state of consciousness, you can practically apply this process into your life and manifest those things that are true for you. It's all creation, and while you're here on earth, you have the power to access creativity to the same degree as anybody else. It all comes from the same source.

For any of you that maybe confused, obviously, this creation process is running parallel to you actually putting in the work. Your goals and dreams aren't going to magically appear out of thin air, as much as you may want them to. Nope, I'm afraid you're going to have be disciplined and have a good work ethic as well, but that can be an enjoyable process too."

Accessing Creativity

"True creativity arises out of presence, and not from the analytical mind." Tyson reinforced to his audience. "When individuals produce works of art that connect, or invent products that fill a void, they are accessing this creative space, either consciously, or unconsciously.

Take a musician as an example. They may write and record without producing anything of meaning, until one day...bang! They're inspired, and produce a song or album that resonates with people, and subsequently becomes popular.

When the artist draws from this creative space, the music, the writing, the designs will flow out of them effortlessly. At these points, they are channelling the creative power that lies in consciousness and are simply expressing it through their craft. These moments of creativity are rare, and most will never experience them.

The musician has gained access to this creative space either consciously by practicing presence and applying the mind like a tool, or unconsciously – almost by accident. Most are connecting with this space unconsciously. They have temporarily experienced an alignment with the creative space that exists in the realm of *presence*.

This becomes particularly apparent when the artist is producing their next project. This is often frustrating for them, as no matter what they do, they cannot create something that lives up to their original work. Unfortunately they are no longer accessing this creative space, and are unaware how to do so. That being said, this creative power is always there, and can be accessed and applied at any time. One simply must understand the process that connects with it.

To access creativity, you must first become present, completely in the *here* and *now* and detached from your thoughts. From here, you apply the mind like a tool, focusing it on the task at hand, letting the analytical side of the mind go and allowing yourself to be guided by intuition – those gut feelings and light bulb moments. This process involves being completely open, allowing yourself to freely make connections and generate ideas. You simply become the vessel for creative flow; you start producing, writing, designing, inventing, dancing or whatever it is, until you have the material that you require. The key is to always remain present and not be taken away into analytical thinking.

Being patient with this process is also essential. When you focus on something long enough, the answer will inevitably come in one form or another. The solution that you require, or the design that you desire, will be highlighted, or pointed to. Be patient and persevere, keep working on whatever you're doing. Trust and have faith that the inspiration will come.

This is where people often become disheartened in the process. They don't see the results straight away, and therefore give up on the task before they have tapped into the creative space. Understanding this process allows you to move past these points of frustration and stay focused until the creativity begins to flow.

Once you have produced the material that you require, even if it looks convoluted at first, within it are the jewels essential to your creation. The next step is to mould the material into a format that can be received by your audience. This could be in the form of editing if you're a writer, or refinement through different media if you're a designer.

Once tailored and released, that's when the magic happens. The product will embody a high level of truth and connect with people in ways that only true art can."

TYSON & JOEY

12

Discipline

For the next few weeks, Tyson and Joey wrote full-time. They worked out of the campus library, which had all the resources they needed. At night, Tyson made brief trips back to Trentan to check on his family and provide them with money to buy food and pay bills. Thankfully, Joey had offered to support them while they were working on the book.

While they worked, it was clear that Joey didn't have the same level of discipline as Tyson. Even with his renewed state of consciousness, he couldn't remain focussed for long periods of time. He would inevitably become distracted by the internet or his smartphone; anything to take him away from the task at hand. He soon realised that discipline didn't come naturally; it was something that was trained and established over time.

Tyson, on the other hand, was like a disciplined soldier. Completely absorbed in the project. His self-restraint had been forged through his time on the streets, and through his rigorous boxing training. He also had experience establishing it within others, as it was fundamental to running a successful crew.

Tyson knew that in order to produce the manuscript in a timely manner, he would have to approach the project in the same way. He knew that, without discipline, their vision would never amount to anything, and the window of opportunity would close. He was well aware that Joey would struggle with this. But knew it was fundamental to his personal growth that he established it within him. That way he could apply it to all aspects of his life.

"Let's get back to work," Tyson said firmly. "This book ain't gonna write itself."

Joey sluggishly stood up from the table where they had been eating lunch and followed Tyson back to the library. "I'm right behind ya, boss."

He was struggling to keep up with the demanding schedule that Tyson had set. Tyson was being very direct and hard to keep him on task. Not only was this making sure that the manuscript was being developed as planned, but it was also breaking Joey's old habits of laziness that had been unconsciously established. Growing up privileged, he had it easy.

As Tyson pushed him to stay focused and be disciplined, Joey could feel himself breaking through his own mental barriers and beginning to establish a strong work ethic. A process he found to be incredibly rewarding.

"You can talk about discipline and hard work all you want, but until you actually apply yourself and do it, it really means nothing doesn't it?" Joey acknowledged.

"You're absolutely right," Tyson replied. "Discipline is something you do even when the mind refuses to. It's about breaking through the mental barriers. Again, staying present is fundamental to this. It stops you from being taken over by the mind and it's limitations, and allows you to stay focused when others become distracted."

The manuscript started to evolve organically. It narrated the story of Tyson's life on the streets, and detailed how adversity had brought him into a state of enlightenment. The chapters that followed reiterated his teachings to Joey, shedding light on the cause of peoples suffering and pointing to presence as being the key to salvation.

Tyson's story flowed out of him as fast as he could type. Joey could hardly keep up with the editing. While writing, Tyson stayed completely in the *now*, detached from the mind and connected to the creative source that is consciousness. Like a vessel, he let the creative energy flow through him and spill out onto the page. In many ways, the story wrote itself.

Tyson could feel change emerging in his life. He was transcending his environment and evolving into a new space that was in line with his true purpose.

Since he was old enough to remember, he had been involved in crime in one way or another. He was indoctrinated into the lifestyle, and knew no better. It wasn't until he grew older that he began to see the conditioning of his environment, and saw clearly how it kept people stuck in a cycle. Tyson had dreamed of transcending the environment like many others, but never knew how.

Little did he know, adversity was to be his greatest gift. A new way of being emerged within, one that connected him to something far greater than anything the material world could ever offer.

Once he understood the truth, that presence was the gateway to his salvation. There was no more dreaming and wishing things would change; instead, there was a knowing that change *would* happen in time, as long as he stayed in the moment and trusted his instincts. Although the mind resisted, he embraced his reality, even on the darkest days.

Now, here he was. Writing his story, and in the process breaking through the glass ceiling of his environment. The opportunity had finally arrived, and to him he knew it was all predestined. The chance meeting with Joey, the teachings, and then the book idea; it was all part of life's greater plan. The necessary change was now in motion.

Stopping the story once more, Tyson felt the need to

elaborate on a key point. Taking a sip of water and sitting himself back down on the stool, he began to discuss the topic of process.

Embrace the Process

"There's a process to everything we do in life," Tyson reinforced to the audience. "Whether it be completing a qualification, establishing a relationship or getting in shape. Each has its own unique path. Although, for many of us it moves too slowly, we want things to happen *now*. We want to skip the progression, and get to the finish line. Achieve our goals without taking the necessary steps to get there. Especially in these modern times, where we are bombarded with get rich quick schemes, and idolise the overnight success story.

You have to embrace the process, however. There are no shortcuts when it comes to truly fulfilling your goals. Be patient, and recognise that hard work will pay off when the time is right; things will fall into place when they are supposed to, not when you want them to. Much easier said than done, I know," Tyson said as he began to recollect on personal experience. "It can be daunting thinking about the time and discipline required to succeed. Therefore, it's understandable why people want to speed things up.

Writing my book had a process. Planning, drafting,

editing, publishing, marketing and many more detailed elements that were essential in bringing the manuscript to life. Countless times I wanted to press fast-forward and release it even when I knew it wasn't ready. My mind desperately wanted to feel the success of it there and then, long before it was in any shape to spark interest. I resisted. I knew that each little step was critical to the quality of the end product, and needed to be respected. More importantly, I trusted that when the time was right, the success my mind so desperately craved would be recognised. Not before, and not after.

Staying present was essential to this. To fully engage with the many steps that it took to write the book, I had to detach from the urgency of the mind and give myself to the *now*. Only then was I able to achieve the task at hand and have clarity about what I needed to do next. It was an organic process from there, slowly but surely I was guided towards my goal, meeting the necessary milestones along the way.

Without presence, the mind will take over and grow frustrated that results are not happening fast enough. As a result, you will end up taking action out of this space, skipping critical tasks to reach the finish line. Then you get there ... and nothing happens. The end product does not live up to the quality that you envisioned. It was undermined by your lack of patience. Know this, the difference between success and failure is in the detail. To get that detail right, you must respect the process.

So I urge you to take your time in whatever you set out to achieve in life. Embrace the journey that it takes to get there. Have discipline and a solid work ethic, but don't rush. That will only compromise the goal. Train yourself to take pleasure in the process by giving it your full attention, and soon you will realise that fulfilment does not come at the finish line. It comes in the many steps along the way." Diversion concluded, Tyson returned to the story of him and Joey.

One evening, after a long day of writing and editing, Tyson and Joey decided to take a break from it all. They went to a local restaurant not far from the university that catered for students and young professionals working in the area. It was completely normal to Joey; he had been coming to the place for years. For Tyson, however, it was all new. He wasn't used to dining in restaurants just because he was hungry, or hanging with people from the suburbs. He was from Trentan, the roughest neighbourhood in the city. Although he enjoyed the new experience, he still felt like an outsider looking in on a different world.

"Man, what a trip it is being out here. I know it's all part of the plan, but it's going to take me some time to adjust to this new way of living. It's all in complete contrast to my old life in Trentan." Tyson said as he leaned back in his chair and looked around the restaurant.

Joey could feel what Tyson was trying to say, something he had been ignorant to. "Hey man, I'm sorry if this is all a bit much sometimes, I forget you're not use to this environment. I'm so comfortable hanging out with you, it feels as though we've known each other for years. The reality is we're from different worlds...I realise that."

Tyson smiled and reached over and patted Joey on the shoulder. "It's all good, bro. I've got to embrace the change and not fear it. People are afraid of change, and that's the reason they stand still. They never allow themselves to transcend. You have to embrace change. It's completely necessary to evolve your consciousness and life situation."

Even though Joey lived a comfortable life, he felt as though he needed to transcend his environment also. This didn't make sense to him, and he felt embarrassed expressing it to Tyson.

"I don't want to come across sounding ungrateful, but I have strong urge to leave my life behind as well. In many ways, I feel conditioned by the materialistic way of living that comes with growing up privileged. I'm more aware of it now than ever; the egotistic nature of it all makes me incredibly uncomfortable. I can't go back to living the way I was."

"It's all part of your evolution, Joey. In many ways,

you are still in the infant stages of your journey. Purging yourself of the conditioning and bringing in a new way of being that is divorced from ego. You don't have to move to downtown Trentan to escape it. You just have to embrace your environment as I did, and the necessary change will come. You have to embrace every last bit of it, look at everything that makes you uncomfortable directly in the eye, and accept it. From there the necessary change will come."

Tyson reiterated to Joey that there was a divine plan for all of us, and that the only way for it to come into fruition was by accepting your reality without resistance. Only then would the path begin to clarify. He reinforced that the journey on the material plan was always secondary to the primary focus of one's life, which was staying present.

"For the majority of people, their focus is not where it should be," Tyson said. "Most are caught up with what is happening in their life situation and lose all connection with the present moment. When this happens, they often become frustrated by the lack of real change. They stay trapped within the conditioned cycles of the mind. When you are conscious of this, you will know to give yourself to the present moment at these times and be patient while things re-balance. From this space the guidance will come, and provide you with whatever is necessary for your life situation. It's all about getting the focus right.

Seeing your life situation as secondary can be a difficult concept to grasp however, especially for people who seek their identity through it."

Joey had struggled with this initially. However, as he began to witness his life situation improve as a by-product of giving himself to the present moment, he knew it was the truth. There were still many questions though.

"I understand what you're saying, and I'm beginning to see how life flows when I stay present. But we will all inevitably experience bad situations at one time or another; it's unavoidable. So what is happening at these times? Do we still embrace them as we would positive situations?" Joey asked.

Tyson could see Joey's confusion and tried to clarify it for him. "Good question. From the perspective of the analytical mind, so called 'bad situations' are exactly that. They hinder your life situation in some way. If you seek your identity through your life situation, then it is an attack on your identity.

From the perspective of presence, you know this is untrue. The 'bad situation' is simply an event that is happening on the material plane, which as I explained earlier is only secondary to your primary focus, which is the present moment itself. Are you following?

But here's where you will see the importance of

these so-called 'bad situations', if you are looking at them from a conscious perspective. Each experience on the material plane is a chance to elevate your state of consciousness and bring yourself further into the *now*. In many ways life is giving you whatever experience is necessary for this to happen."

Evolution of Consciousness

Stopping the narrative once more, Tyson began to explore another concept with the audience. "Evolution of consciousness refers to your state of presence," he said. "Your connection to the *here* and the *now*. An evolving state, which is ultimately the process of dis-identifying from the mind.

Life is giving you whatever experience is needed for this to this happen. These experiences will encompass different areas, and will play on your insecurities. Whether it be related to health, relationship, family or career, a situation will be brought into your life that generates fear, anxiety, depression or any other so-called negative emotions.

The situations I'm talking about are those that generate psychological fear and unrest, rather than an immediate real threat. From a conscious perspective they are gifts, as they give you a chance to evolve your state of presence.

An example could be an addiction to drugs. The situation causes a tremendous amount of psychological unrest, which is only eased through the taking of drugs and feeding the addiction.

Alternatively, if the person could take a step back from the situation and see it as a chance to elevate their state of being, they could approach it in a different way. From a conscious perspective, you approach the addiction with presence. Disconnecting from the mind and sitting with the urges, allowing them to simply wash over you. Incredibly difficult to do, but every time the person sits with the addiction and feels it in its entirety, letting the urges come and eventually pass, they are becoming stronger. Not only are they breaking the addiction, but they are also elevating their state of consciousness. This is just one example of how a so-called 'negative' experience can be used to build upon the foundation of presence in your life.

Alas, the majority of people don't see these experiences from this perspective. They will try easing the psychological unrest by feeding the addiction, or distracting themselves temporarily. You must take the opposite approach and face your reality head-on from a state of presence. Know that the experience is ultimately good. Sit with the strong emotions and create room for a higher state of consciousness to come into your life."

13

The Final Step

Joey had undergone huge changes since meeting Tyson. He had first encountered the other man racked with anxiety and depression, with no knowledge of who he really was. He was now aware of his true nature, and was in the process of evolving his state of consciousness. Tyson had been guiding him through this transition and reinforcing the teachings when he slipped back into his mind-identified state. But he couldn't be there forever. It was inevitable that they would part ways and continue on their individual journeys. For Joey, this would be essential. He needed to swim alone without the support of Tyson. This would be the final step in his evolution; to take the lessons learned, and apply them without the support of his teacher.

Tyson began to explain this to Joey as they worked on the manuscript. "Do you know what your next step in the evolutionary process is?" Tyson asked.

Joey looked back at Tyson trying to figure out where

he was going with this. "I think so," Joey replied. "Like you said, as long as I continue to give myself to the *now*, the inner guidance will come."

Tyson nodded in agreement. "That's right, but you will have to continue to do that alone. My role as your teacher has almost come to an end. Soon, it will be time for you to apply the teachings on your own terms without my support. This is essential for your development. You cannot be dependent on me, Joey. That would defeat the purpose of everything I taught you. You must be independent, and only then can we reconnect. Do you understand what I mean?"

Joey was taken aback by Tyson's comments; he had formed a friendship with him and looked to him for guidance. The thought of having to let this go frightened him. He was scared he might slip into his old ways without Tyson. But he saw the truth in what he was saying. He knew he had to break the dependency to truly live the teachings.

"I understand," Joey replied. "It's hard though, I'm scared I might fall back into the old mind patterns. You've always been there to point them out in me. Without that, how will I know if I'm on the right track?" Joey asked.

Tyson could see Joey's distress. "You will know, brother. When life feels like it's becoming overwhelming, and you feel the anxiety beginning to rise within you, simply take a step back and bring yourself into the now. No matter what is going on, presence is the answer my friend. Remember the simplicity of it all. Bring yourself into the *now*, and stay there. The inner guidance will come when it's supposed to. Always remember this, Joey; it's so simple, but so easy to overlook in times of distress. As long as you trust in the *now* and fully give yourself to it, you will always stay on the right track."

Joey felt a sense of relief with Tyson's words. "Thank you. Sincerely. It's that one truth that sits at the core of all your teachings. That's all I have to remember."

Tyson nodded in agreement. "That's right, the simple truth that underpins it all is the only thing that needs to be understood. The metaphors and analogies that make up the rest of the teaching are simply signposts pointing to it. They are necessary in the beginning to get you to the core. But once you have connected with it, they are no longer needed."

The first draft of the manuscript was almost complete. They had been working on it full-time for months; preparing a presentation to the publishing company that Joey had a connection with. It had developed just as they had envisioned, telling the story of Tyson's life on the streets and reinforcing his message of presence.

Tyson had always told Joey that people come together

for a reason, to help each other to develop and evolve. He knew from his first meeting with Joey that they had something to offer each other, although it wasn't clear from the outset he trusted his instincts. They were from different worlds, but there was a common ground that *change* was necessary. Tyson was living the street life, and was inevitably going to end up dead or in jail. Joey was falling into the black hole of depression and losing all hope.

Two worlds collided, and the necessary change manifested for both. Tyson showed Joey how to connect with peace, and Joey provided Tyson with an opportunity.

They had produced something meaningful in the process, a book with the ability to transform people's lives. Just as the teachings had helped Joey, they had faith it would do the same with others. They knew there were countless people suffering in the same capacity as he was.

To celebrate their joint effort, they decided to go for dinner at one of the finest restaurants in town. It sat at the top of the tallest tower in the city, and had a view for miles.

"Beautiful!" Tyson declared, as he looked out at the city lights, blinking in the night sky. "I can see Trentan from here, just across the river. Coming from that neighbourhood, I never imagined I would be up here dining in such a fine restaurant. I'm not sure I can even pronounce half the things on the menu."

Emotion got the better of Tyson, and he began to shed a few tears. It was a bittersweet moment. He was dining in luxury, but his family and friends were still trapped in poverty across the river. He was hopeful, though. He knew it wouldn't be long until he had his family out, and he could go back and make real change in his community.

Tyson was the change that Trentan needed. He had the potential to teach and inspire the younger generation, and show them that there are other avenues outside of the street life. Most importantly, he could teach people how to connect with inner peace. Show them that even if their reality was grim, there was something far greater beneath the chaos.

Tyson and Joey sat back in their seats and made a toast. "To the next chapter," Joey said aloud.

"To the present moment," Tyson responded.

They clinked their glasses together and began to laugh. "You got me there," Joey said. "After all your preaching, you would think I would have that one figured out by now."

"What can I say, you're a slow learner," Tyson replied. "But on a serious note, cheers to the coming together of two guys from different backgrounds and helping each other to evolve to where they needed to be. Thank you for trusting me, Joey. Not many people would have taken me in like you did. I'm forever grateful for the opportunity you have given me, and I will never forget that."

Tyson's words touched him. "It's my pleasure. I feel like, for the first time in my life, I'm doing something meaningful. I'm forever grateful. I wouldn't be feeling the peace that I do today if it wasn't for your teachings. I was stuck in a dark hole and you showed me how to get out of it. How about we call it even?" Joey responded.

Tyson nodded in agreement. "Sounds good to me. Look out at the vastness of it all," he added as he gazed out into the night sky. "Really makes you feel small in the grand scheme of things. It all comes from the same source, my brother. The source of everything – consciousness itself. It lies underneath all that you see on the material plane. Everything manifests from there. You, me, and the stars that populate the night sky. Makes you appreciate the power of it all doesn't it? You Joey, you can access that power too. As long as you're connected with the present moment it will flow through you into everything you do."

Eternal Present

Tyson took a final deep breath as he prepared to conclude his speech.

"Presence is eternal," he announced through a cracking voice. "It's the space that everything comes from, and everything eventually returns to. When you're connected to this space, you realise that your mortality is simply on the material plane and that, at your core, you never die.

Our life here on earth is relative to that of a ripple on top of the ocean. A temporary event on the surface of something immeasurably greater. The ripple comes from the ocean, and will *return* to the ocean. Therefore, to identify with it, and look for yourself in it, cuts you off from the source from where it arises.

To know this is freeing. It makes you realise that you are not defined by your temporary existence on earth. It's simply an expression on the surface, which can either be joyful or full of suffering, depending on your understanding of it. Always remember; when the ripple knows its connection to the ocean, it can do amazing things.

Knowing that you are part of something bigger gives you inner peace and an appreciation for your own humanity. From this space, death is only the end of your physical form. It has no implications on your true existence, which is consciousness itself."

Tyson let his words settle as he made his way to the side of the stage for one last mouthful of water.

"And that concludes this talk! I'd like to thank you all for attending tonight, and for buying the book of course. I'll be signing copies in the foyer, but first I think we have a little time for questions. Yes, you, at the back in the green shirt? What's your name, and your question?"

A young man of a similar age to Tyson stood and shuffled from foot to foot.

"Um, yeah, hi. My name is Sammy. I'm feeling a little lost, and wondered if you provide one-on-one mentoring…?"

Acknowledgements

Thank you to all the influences that have helped shape this book. Firstly, to my battle with mental illness, although I nearly lost to you I am grateful for the experience. It was necessary for my personal growth and the writing of this book. Thank you to my family who were there for me in those dark times. Your support and unconditional love will never be forgotten. To my brothers, you know who you are, I have learnt so much from each and every one of you. To the countless people who have shown me guidance along the way, thank you. And to Amy, your patience and companionship can never be overlooked. Lastly, Greg the editor, thank you for helping to bring the manuscript to where it needed to be.

Made in the USA
Lexington, KY
03 April 2017